Be Careful What You Promise . . .

Slowly I brought my hands up against the place where she was pressing hers. But as soon as I touched the glass, I felt such a pang inside that I almost yanked my hands away.

"Done!" she exclaimed, before I could say anything about changing my mind. The bargain was made, and there was such happiness dancing in her eyes that I just couldn't go back on it.

DON'T LOOK IN THE MIRROR

DON'T LOOK IN THE MIRROR

Larry Weinberg

To Dori, Mark, and Brian

Chapter 1

I remember a dream I was having. In it, I was a very small girl again, playing on the rug next to my bed with large pieces of a jigsaw puzzle. A loud alarm clock rang like crazy somewhere, and I kept wondering why my mommy or daddy didn't shut it off. The alarm must have been for them, because I was still much too young to have to go to school.

The ringing was so annoying that I really had to concentrate to fit in the different pieces of my puzzle. So far I had put together the top of a girl's head, with her brown hair hanging down in bangs to her eyebrows. I started to work on one side of her face, but all I got was a lot more falling hair. I mean, it covered everything!

I still wasn't getting a good idea of what the girl looked like. I fitted in the nose and one eye. It was such a sad-looking eye that I began to wonder what in the world was wrong with this girl. It was the next piece of the puzzle that finally showed me some skin. I fitted in the chin and—oh my God, look at those *pimples!*

Red, raw, oozy, and there were *hundreds* of them, maybe *thousands!* No wonder she was hiding behind all that hair. Now that I looked more closely, I could see even more pimples under the strands. Yuck! What if even touching the puzzle pieces would make some of the pimples come off on me?

I jumped away from the puzzle, but I could already tell I was breaking out. My forehead felt like snakes were slithering on it. Hot pimples rose like volcanoes on my chin. My whole face itched! It was so horrible, I burst into tears. Why was this happening to me? Wasn't I too young? Wasn't I still a very little girl?

No! Suddenly I was that girl in the puzzle, and that stupid alarm was ringing for me! I woke up with real tears in my eyes, knowing that another long school day of being called "Miss Zits" was ahead of me. If the bathroom mirror didn't show me at least a little improvement, how would I get through the day without killing myself? I walked to the sink, still teary-eyed, and went head-to-head with the mirror on the medicine cabinet.

I blinked, and blinked again, hardly daring to believe what I saw. Furiously I wiped away the last bit of wetness standing between me and twenty-twenty vision before I put my face practically up against the glass. It was true! I felt as if I'd been lit up inside by a bolt of lightning.

"I'm a human being again!" I shouted, rushing into my room and yanking on my clothes. I don't think my feet touched the steps as I flew downstairs yelling,

"Everybody look what's happened to my face!"

"And a lovely face it is, too," declared my father in his soft Irish accent. He put down his teacup as I ran into the kitchen. "A face of enchantment, as I've always said." Planting a kiss on the tip of my nose, he headed for the hallway. "Well, another day, another dollar, minus taxes, of course," he said with a smile. "See my two ladies tonight, and until then, God bless."

I was stunned. "He didn't notice!" But my father was always absentmindedly moving in a fog of his own. My mom turned from the stove. "Didn't notice what, darling?"

"My acne! Look how it's cleared up! Every last hideous, sickening, pus-filled, makes-you-want-to-vomit pimple is gone! They've all disappeared!"

"Oh, let me see!" Mom cried. But when she came closer, a puzzled expression clouded her face, and she started talking in that slow voice of hers that meant something was wrong. "Why, yes. I think that medicine's working. It really does look a bit better."

"A *bit*? What do you mean a *bit*?"

"Well, more than a bit," she said, giving me one of those flustered little smiles that always meant she was being more polite than honest. Then she retreated into her busy-housewife attitude. "You got up late, so sit down quickly or you won't have a chance to eat your oatmeal. Do you want maple syrup?"

I didn't sit. I simply stared at her. "Wait a minute. You actually can't see that all my pimples are gone?"

Now she let her tenderness come out. "Not really, dearest. You must have dreamed they did and then got up believing it."

She started to hug me, but pity wasn't what I needed. "No, that's not what I dreamed! Not at all!" My hands went to my face, and I could have died. The pimples were all still there!

"Alice, if you're not well, maybe you should stay home today." It was an offer she rarely liked to make. I would have jumped at it, but there was only one person I could talk to about this, and Wendy was on her way to school.

"You know what, Mom? I think you're right. I must have dreamed it."

"Dreams can seem so real sometimes," she agreed, as I walked to the hallway.

"If you're leaving without eating, Alice, take a banana!"

But I was already at the closet getting my coat. Suddenly I became aware of my reflection in the long hallway mirror that stretched along the wall to the front door. The image was turning, of course, just as I was. As my reflection faced me, it showed all of my pimples, every single one. But then—and this certainly wasn't happening on my hideous mug—the mouth of my reflection opened into a gorgeous smile, the head gave a toss that sent its hair flying, and all of those zits completely vanished!

I think I gasped. This was crazy! I had to get out of the house. But as I rushed toward the door, the image in the mirror moved along with me. Not wildly like I did, oh, no! She was elegant, and so cool she could have been a model in a fashion show. That was exactly how she was wearing my baggy, droopy coat! And *she* was certainly having fun. In fact, when we reached for the knob together, I was positive she winked at me!

Believe me, I couldn't get through that door fast enough. As I ran down the stone steps and along the path to the street, I didn't even notice how hard the rain was pouring down until I was already halfway to the corner.

A huge puddle ahead of me made me stop short. There was a shine on it from a streetlight that hadn't gone off yet. Before I could make my way around it, my own reflection grinned up at me, still looking perfect. Then she blew me a kiss!

"Just leave me alone!" I screamed. To prove I meant it, I stomped right into the face. Of course, that soaked me, but it also scattered her. I ran to the bus stop thinking—God only knows what I was thinking—as the bus pulled up.

Climbing aboard, I remembered another big problem—the promise I'd made to Wendy about a certain brave act I was going to perform on the bus today, no matter what. She called it my "facing rejection time." Or, rather, my telling myself I'd been rejected by David DeWitt before I actually was.

There he sat—"sprawled" would be a better word for it—in his usual seat on the right side of the aisle two rows from the back. His endlessly long legs had galloped so many miles over the football fields that his jeans were skintight over his calves. A thickly knitted sweater covered the big muscles of his passing arm. The sweater was coal black, like his hair and eyes, which, as usual, shone with a faraway look that made people give him the row to himself.

I suppose I wasn't the only girl who became a complete emotional wreck every time she saw David. But the other girls didn't have a friend who said, "If people can go to church and talk to the Lord, they can certainly say something to David NitWitt."

I didn't much care for Wendy calling him that. I mean, how can someone be dumb when he was almost unanimously elected Student Council president and his ambition is to be governor! But I did get her point, which was that I had been shy, especially with guys, a lot longer than I'd been pimpled. I could not hide behind my zitface if I was ever going to shake that problem. Not that Wendy expected me to convert David DeWitt into my adoring boyfriend. She just wanted me to prove that I could say hello to him like one human being to another!

"And what if he ignores me?" I'd asked so meekly that Wendy lost her patience.

"Then just tell him to pull in his feet! Look, Alice, it's not what *he* does, it's what *you* do. The fact that you did something positive is going to make a change for you. Do you see what I mean?"

I did, of course—at least in a way—which is why I'd promised. And here, as they say, was my moment of truth.

In fact, I'd made up my mind that not only was I going to say something to him, I'd also slip right into the empty seat next to him.

Gathering my willpower as I moved along, I walked slowly past each row until I came to the place in the middle of the aisle where David's legs were crossed at the ankles. Then I came to a halt . . . took a very deep breath . . . squinched my brows into a look of determination . . . felt like I was going to die . . . told myself it was nonsense to be so afraid of a little thing like this . . . and did the same weak-minded thing I'd always done. I stepped over his legs and dropped into the row behind him—but on the other side of the aisle so I could sneak little glances at him.

All right, I was a coward. It was humiliating. I felt so horrible, I shut myself down as only Alice Shea knows how to do and went into such a complete funk that I didn't notice anything that was going on around me. It wasn't until the rain stopped and the morning sun put a glare on the windows that I felt a light in my eyes. I looked up and saw that it was coming not from the sun, but from a smile. That smile was reflecting from the window across from me—but one row ahead. In other words, it was from *David's* window. His reflection was in it, but the person doing the smiling was the other me!

They were together in that reflection. They were actually sitting beside each other. He had his arm over her shoulder, and he was gazing at her like he was Christopher Columbus just discovering the New World!

Now she was leaning toward him, like they were just about to kiss. But first she glanced past his shoulder and lifted a hand. What nerve! She was waving at me, and her look clearly said, "See how easy it is, you weakling?"

So she was following me. She wasn't going to stop until . . . what? Until I was ready to be taken off to a padded cell?

I had to keep from seeing her until I could get myself together. I closed my eyes and wouldn't look at anything until the bus stopped and I heard the kids getting off. Even then, I kept myself from looking anywhere but at the floor as I walked to the front. I was especially careful not to catch a glimpse of myself in the driver's rearview mirror as I got off.

Then I had to cope with the glass in the school

door. Just before there was any chance of seeing her in it, I spun around and stepped through backward, telling everyone who was coming in behind me, "Hey, didn't you hear? School's canceled and I'm leaving."

Someone said, "You wish!"

Once inside the building, I made a dash for the lockers at the far end of the hall. When I'm worked up about anything I get red in the face. Wendy, who was waiting there, must have seen me looking like I was on fire.

Right away her eyes lit up. Because she's so small and I'm so stringy tall, she had to bounce up on her toes to give me a hug. "My God, you did it!" she whispered in my ear. "I'm so proud of you!"

Then she was down on her feet, leading me away from the lockers and all the eyes and ears around us to our confiding place at the end of the corridor.

"So tell me how you started the conversation. Did you really sit down next to him?"

Before I could open my mouth, I suddenly reminded myself that we were next to a window. It was made with a bumpy kind of glass, and there was only a dim courtyard behind it, so maybe there wasn't going to be any kind of reflection there. But this creepy feeling of being watched came over me, so I grabbed Wendy by the wrist and made her run.

"Alice! What are you doing?"

"Can't talk here," I mumbled. "Got to find

someplace safe." The janitor was just coming out of one of the storage closets. The second he turned away from it, I yanked Wendy inside and closed the door. We stood there in darkness until she pulled the string dangling from the light fixture on the ceiling. "What do you mean, 'safe'? Why are you trembling?" she asked.

"Look, maybe it's nothing," I said edgily.

"Maybe *what's* nothing? Why are you so scared?"

"You don't really want to hear!"

"I don't?"

"No! And will you please take off those eyeglasses?"

"You mean I don't want to see, either?"

"It's not a joke," I snapped. "Believe me, it's not funny!"

"I believe you. What's not funny?"

"Wendy, I'm having a breakdown!"

"Is it a good breakdown or a bad breakdown?"

"I . . . uh . . ." It was such a ridiculous question that I exploded. "Now what are *you* talking about?"

"I mean is it because you spoke to David and found out he's a hopeless case? Or you still couldn't speak to him and now *you're* a hopeless case? That way, I'll know which pieces of your mind I have to help you pick up."

"You're being picky again, Wendy. This isn't the time to take anything apart when I'm already apart! I mean, my God, my own image has rebelled against me."

18

"Well, that's nothing to be upset about. I mean, it's great news. I've been telling you for a long time you need to get a better image of yourself."

"I'm not talking about that kind of image!"

"You're not? Okay. Stop shouting or we're going to have the custodian or somebody coming in here. Can you calm down?"

"Yes, yes," I rasped. "I'm calming down." I took a deep breath and held it in my lungs like they do in yoga.

"So then, is it all right if I put my glasses back on?"

"No!" I screamed, expelling the air.

"No. Okay, well, that's all right, too. What I can't see we'll do in Braille." Wendy took me by my hands and squinted up at me. "What kind of image are you talking about?"

"The one that you see when you look at yourself in a mirror."

"Okay," she said very slowly, giving me the strangest look. "So how did the image of you that you saw in the mirror rebel?"

"It isn't just one mirror, Wendy," I said, trembling. "It's *all* the mirrors. And anything that can be turned into one. I'm not me anymore, Wendy. I can't control it. It smiles when I don't smile. It moves when I don't move. It stands better and it walks better and it doesn't have any zits!'

"Oh," she said, as if she understood perfectly, although I could see perfectly well that she didn't.

"Oh what?"

"Just oh. Go on."

"And do you know what she did on the bus?"

"She?"

"The *other* Alice!"

"No, what did she do?" Wendy said in a let's-humor-the-poor-girl tone of voice.

"She sat down next to David and talked to him, and she practically made out with him!"

"You're kidding me?"

"No. I'm not kidding."

"And you saw all this with your own eyes?"

"Yes."

"While you were sitting *where?*"

"You know where."

"Okay, so you didn't sit down with him. You went to your own seat behind him."

"And across the aisle, yes," I agreed.

"And then you saw *them?*"

"That's what I keep telling you! They were sitting together."

"Who were?"

I was shouting again. "David and . . . and me."

"So you *imagined* you saw yourself with him?"

By this time I was grinding my teeth. "I didn't imagine it, Wendy. They really were both there together."

"In the same row?"

"Wendy, you are supposed to have a genius IQ."

"Sometimes it slips."

"I could only see them in the *window*," I said carefully. "Two reflections. Hers and his."

Wendy held up her hand for silence and paused to think. Somewhere down the hall, a bell rang.

"Now that I've had a chance to *reflect* upon this—" Wendy started.

"No jokes, Wendy, please!"

"God forbid. I mean the most important thing about keeping a mental breakdown going is not having a sense of humor about it."

"Okay, okay. You're right. So what do you think?"

"It's no big deal, Alice. You've been obsessed with looking at yourself in mirrors for so long, and wishing for so long to find a change in yourself, that your mind's finally giving you what you want by playing tricks on you."

"That," I said with a sneer, "is what my mother said after the first time it happened!"

"Just because she said it doesn't make it wrong. She knows you've been dwelling on this just as much as I do. And it ought to be your wakeup call, girl. Your own system is signaling you to cut out the self-consciousness and get on with your life."

"You think that's what it is?"

"It's just like a burning pain warning you to get away from the stove!"

I was feeling so pathetically tiny, I positively squeaked like a mouse. "You don't think it's too late?"

"No! If it were, you wouldn't be so upset about hallucinating."

"That's what it is? I've been *hallucinating?*" I repeated in a trembling voice.

Wendy's calling it that was no different, I suppose, from telling me I'd been seeing things. Yet somehow the word *hallucinating* sounded much more frightening to me. Wendy must have seen how upset I was. She bit her lip and said, "I had a big hand in this, you know. I pushed you awful hard to talk to David when you really weren't ready for it. Now I'm just so sorry."

I touched her shoulder. "Well, you shouldn't be."

"Now, listen, Alice. We're going to get through this thing together. You know that, right?"

I took a deep breath. "I . . . I hope so. But what can I do?"

"For one thing, you can lay off mirrors."

I let what she said sink in, and suddenly I began to feel much lighter. "You know what, Wendy? That's exactly what I'm going to do!"

"Fantastic!" she said, moving past me to shove the door open. "In case you didn't notice, that bell stopped ringing long ago. Gotta run. Catch you later in Signing."

But she stopped in front of me, fumbling with her glasses. As she put them on, I saw them flash into life.

In each of the lenses was a reflection of me. One of them was exactly like me and had all my zits. But in the other, Perfect Girl tilted her head to the side and brushed back her hair. Then her smiling lips formed the silent words "Hello, Alice."

It gave me such a jolt that I jumped back. Before Wendy could ask what had happened, I whirled away from her and ran to my homeroom.

Chapter 2

Halfway through my first-period class, Social Studies, I finally began to pay attention. A discussion was going on about whether there was any kind of freedom of speech that shouldn't be allowed in a democracy. Soon it became an argument about whether the principal was right to suspend a student for swearing in the cafeteria after she'd been warned three times to settle down.

On one side a bunch of people said no, because everybody swore outside of school anyhow and swearing was just a way to express a point of view strongly. Then the only guy wearing a shirt and tie raised his hand to say that there was nothing wrong with setting rules in a place of education—as long as you were allowed to make your points without using four-letter words in every sentence.

Some people nodded or looked like they were about to say they agreed with him. But right away a storm of sneers and groans of "I can't believe this!" came down around his head. Then the poor guy got accused of wanting to see "the Speech Police following everybody through the halls taking down names!"

Personally, I thought it was wrong to suspend that

girl for swearing. But then most of the very people who were so hot for total freedom of speech had just bullied almost everybody who disagreed with them into shutting up. It was so unfair that I knew I should have gotten up to say so—even though I was on their side of the argument.

Yet I didn't. Why not? First of all, because of the shyness I'd always had. Second, I didn't want to draw attention to my zits. So I went back to feeling lousy. And that's how I felt till I got to my next class, which was Signing.

Right away, Wendy and I paired off. Crossing our arms at the wrists and pressing our hands to our chests, we made the love sign to each other. That was our usual best-friends greeting, but this time hers felt especially welcome.

Using signs for whole words when we knew them and spelling them out with our fingers when we didn't, we mostly talked about how I was feeling. There was nothing wrong with being scared, Wendy told me. She advised me to keep reminding myself that I was not alone and that I had someone who was there for me. If I just allowed things to settle down in my mind and tried to find a little faith in myself, I'd see that things would work out fine. Before we parted I touched my fingertips to my lips in the "thank you" sign at least a dozen times. I went off to my math class breathing almost like a normal person.

Laser printouts were on our desks when I got there. It was a surprise quiz. Ordinarily I'd hate that, but now it gave me something outside of myself to concentrate on. I dove right in and was just coming to the end of it when I started to hear a sharp little *tap-tap, tap-tap*, like somebody was rapping the point of a pencil on the desk. It bothered me, and I looked around to find out who was doing it. But I seemed to be the only person paying any attention to it. Right away that gave me just a little bit of a shiver. I tried to shake it off, but I couldn't—not when that rapping got even louder.

Now it seemed to be coming from the wall across from the windows. My eyes were pulled upward toward the clock. What made my throat begin to tighten was that until now that clock had always been silent. I forced myself to look straight at it.

That other Alice was on the glass covering, and the pencil she was using to tap on it was the reflection of my own. Now that she'd gotten my attention, she started using the pencil to point at the door. I was being given instructions from my own image. She wanted me to leave the room!

At first I thought: *Not a chance!* But then I realized that, once and for all, this had to stop. I would *make* it stop. I jumped up and was halfway across the floor before the teacher called to me. I whirled around, asked permission to leave, dropped my quiz down on

27

her desk, rushed out into the hall, and broke into a breakneck dash for the girls' room. I went face-to-face with my breakaway image in the big mirror over the sinks.

"I'd like you to call me Alicia," she said pleasantly in *my* voice. "I think it's far more sophisticated than plain old Alice, don't you?"

"I'm in big trouble," I mumbled. I plunged my face into cold water to see if the shock would bring me around.

"Make sure you dry our ears, too," she told me as I reached half-blindly for a paper towel.

"Why is this happening to me?" I moaned.

"Because you need me."

"I *need* to go crazy?"

"We're not crazy at all."

"We? What's this *we*?" I screamed as I looked up into her sweet and happy, peaches-and-cream face. "You're not a *you*. You're an *it*! You get it? An *it*!"

"Yes," she sighed. "That was certainly true during all those years when I was simply your reflection and had no being of my own. But now I'm real, thanks to all the energy and hope you fed into me at the mirrors. I exist, and instead of being frightened or angry you ought to be glad about it. Why else would I be here except to help you become exactly like this? So why don't you take a good look and tell me if you like what you see."

She was turning around slowly to give me a view of her hairstyle and her upright posture when the bathroom door burst open and Wendy rushed in, saying she had heard something.

It wasn't until later that I found out she'd seen me in the hall from her Science class, run out to look for me, and finally heard my voice coming from here. I didn't question her arrival; I was much too anxious to have her see for herself. I pointed at the mirror. "Look at her turning around!" I cried.

"I'm looking," she said ever so gently. "And all I see is you pointing at your own reflection."

It was true! The zits, the hair, the posture, the expression on the face—they were all exactly mine! An ordinary mirror image, nothing more!

"But she *was* different from me, Wendy, I swear it. She talked to me, and she called herself Alicia, and . . . Hey! Didn't you just tell me you heard voices?"

"I said I heard *your* voice," she replied.

"Well, she uses my voice." Now I was pleading. "Didn't you hear anything she said?"

"What I heard was, 'and tell me if you like what you see.'"

"That's it! Now, would I say that to myself?"

"If you were talking to yourself, you might. People do that all the time."

"I thought you were in my corner!"

"I am," Wendy said. "But do you want a friend

who's straight with you or not? Should I pretend that I don't believe this is all in your head? Well, if I thought there was no hope for you, then that's what I suppose I'd have to do. But all that's happened is that you're just caught up with this. The idea is stuck in your mind like one of those songs you can't get rid of. It's like all those years I kept thinking I was dumb, no matter what scores I got on my IQ tests. This idea's got a hold on you, that's all, and you have to break it."

My legs felt weak, and I sank back against a sink. "So what do I have to do, go to a shrink?"

"Whatever it takes, Alice! Hey, therapists aren't so bad. At least not all of them. I've gone to a couple myself."

"I know that. I didn't mean—"

"I might even become one someday." She grinned at me. "Then you could become my first patient."

"I can't wait that long, Wendy."

"I know. I'm sorry if I'm making jokes. This sure isn't funny."

"No. Not a bit."

"Come on. I'm gonna take you home."

But I didn't want that. I'd need a nurse's note, and there'd have to be all kinds of explanations for Wendy to be allowed to go with me. And how would we get home—take a cab? Who had the money for that? Besides, I didn't want to be alone in the house with those mirrors. But it would be even worse if my mother was still home and we had to tell her the whole story. She'd get all worked up, and I'd soon be taking care of *her!*

"I'm going back to class," I said.

"You sure you can do it?"

I nodded. "You can't watch me all the time, Wendy. I'm just going to do my best to stay calm, no matter what. See you in the cafeteria?"

Wendy frowned. "Well, I guess I could call it off."

"What?"

"I promised to tutor a kid in study hall. He's got this test coming up later and he's really sinking fast."

"No, no, you go do it. I'll be okay."

"You sure?"

"The only thing I'm sure about," I said grimly, "is that I'm gonna try."

Well, it wasn't easy getting through the day, especially when I caught sight of "Alicia" in some way or other. But something had changed about her. That big, lighthearted smile was gone. She was gazing at me thoughtfully, and sometimes I even noticed an expression in her glittering eyes that filled me with inexplicable sadness.

On the way home, the sunlight came into the bus on the side where I was sitting. I felt a warm glow settle on the windowpane next to my cheek, and I heard her voice softly in my ear. "So far I've been

31

shocking you, Alice, and I don't want to do that anymore. Just please listen to what I have to say, then decide for yourself if you want me to be your friend. I'll leave it to you after that and never bother you again if you don't want me to. Fair enough?"

I nodded, and she went on.

"Since it's you who created me, please ask yourself this: Why would I have any reason to be here except to help you become everything you desperately want to be? This face of mine would really be your face, if your skin was clear. The way you see me walk and hold myself is the way you would, if you had the self-assurance. And the changes that I've made with my hair, the touchups here and there, are all changes you could make.

"But you don't know how, and that's because of the one big difference between us. You see, Alice, while you've been so tied up in knots about yourself that you don't look around you, I've been studying the girls who know how to carry themselves and make the most of how they look. I study the boys and see what reaches them, even the faraway-in-the-distance ones like David DeWitt. You keep telling yourself that everything is going to change for you once you get rid of your acne. But do you know what? You've been hiding behind those pimples."

I turned to her, fuming. But she didn't back off.

"Yes, you have, Alice. You're not going to clear

them up with any of the medication you've been taking or the glycerine soaps or the lotions you've been smearing on. It's only going to happen after you begin to feel so good about yourself that you stop sending ugliness signals to your body chemistry."

Her pop psychology irritated me. I shut my eyes and sank deeper into my seat. "This is stupid," I hissed. "I don't want to hear it."

"Well, good-bye then," I heard her say after a while. "I tried my best. You won't see me anymore. Have a good life."

Later, when I looked into the window, all I saw were the streets on the other side of it. That, and the see-through ghost of my hideous zitface.

So Alicia was gone. What a relief! But that feeling lasted only until I went into my house, looked in the hallway mirror—and discovered that I was missing, too. I couldn't see myself! It was the same upstairs with the bathroom mirror. I stared at it until I was pop-eyed, but there wasn't a thing to see in it except the wall behind me.

As far as mirrors were concerned, I didn't exist.

Chapter 3

Of course, the first thing I did was call Wendy and tell her what had happened. She promised to cycle over right away. When half an hour passed without her showing up, I called again. Her mother, very agitated, was just dashing out of the house. Wendy had had an accident rushing to get here on half-dark streets that were still wet from the morning rain. The driver of the pickup truck she'd crashed into had taken her to the emergency room. Wendy had injured her leg. As soon as I heard that, I ran downstairs, got on my own bike, and pedaled furiously to the hospital.

As I rolled through the parking lot toward the EMERGENCY sign, I saw Wendy's twisted bike lying against a wall where the driver must have put it. I ran inside just in time to see Wendy, her right leg bandaged, hobbling out on crutches.

I felt so bad I started crying, but her mother told me that Wendy would be fine. She'd only suffered a torn ligament and a sprain. Her mother added, however, that this should be a lesson to the two of us not to get so involved with our personal problems that we paid no attention to the ordinary dangers in life. Wendy never should have run out of the house like that. Just look what her carelessness had nearly caused.

In fact, Mrs. Bauer thought the two of us should "take a breather" and give each other a little space for a while. "Wendy came home from school looking as if the weight of the world was on her shoulders," she said. "Then, ten minutes later, your call came, and it was as if the sky was going to cave in if she didn't throw herself right out of the house to stop it."

By this time we were out the door going toward their minivan, and Wendy was pleading with her mother to cool it. "Oh, I'm very cool," said her mother, though she wasn't. "Alice, you know I've always liked you very much, and I still do. But there are certain problems that maybe you'd be best off relying on your parents to help you solve."

Suddenly I had the horrified thought that she knew about Alicia, but Wendy caught on and shook her head. She also gave me a hurt look, as if I should have known better than to think she'd blab anything like that without my permission.

Now I felt doubly guilty. But all I could do was to carry the broken bike to the back of the minivan and say how sorry I felt about everything.

I could hardly sleep that night for fear of more bad dreams. In the morning, I got up to go to the bathroom feeling like Count Dracula rising from the dead, since vampires also cast no reflections in mirrors.

But there I was again, the typical me. That gave me a little relief until I called Wendy's house to see how she was. Her mother was polite enough with me. Wendy, she said, was still asleep and being kept home from school. She thanked me for calling and would certainly tell Wendy how much I wanted her to get well fast, but for the same reasons she mentioned yesterday, she thought it best that Wendy and I not talk with each other on the phone for a while.

It was beginning to dawn on me by then that, aside from becoming sane again, there was absolutely no reason to feel good about having my zitzy face staring back at me from mirrors. Hallucination or not, the fact is that I'd been shown something better, but I'd walked away from it.

My mood was so bad that when I got onto the bus and saw David DeWitt's dumb legs stretched all over my path as if I didn't exist again, I bent down and grabbed them with both hands and shoved them out of the way!

David twisted in his seat. "Hey!"

"Hay is for horses!" I grunted, moving on.

It wasn't bright of me, it wasn't original. It wasn't anything. But I'd said *something*—though I wouldn't be able to tell Wendy about it, not for days anyway. This time when I dropped into my usual seat, I didn't look at David DeWitt, not once.

Well, maybe *once*. That was when he slid into the

aisle behind me after we pulled up to the school. "Sorry about my feet," he said when we were on the steps getting off. "Just can't keep 'em tucked in there."

He was being *friendly!* "It's-s-s okay," I stammered, ordering myself to get ready to turn around and look at him. I took two or three steps, then turned with my mouth open to say something.

But he wasn't there. Driveway pebbles were crunching under his long, loping steps as he crossed the parking lot. A girl—a senior cheerleader whom everyone called the Student Body—was getting out of her car. She was living proof of the power of Spandex over the male mind, and all the guys near me were gaping. The look she directed toward David DeWitt was making the air between them crackle like those electricity experiments where lightning jumps between two poles.

Well, if he was going into a clinch with her before half the school, I didn't want to see it! So much for our big conversation together. I marched to my homeroom thinking Nature could be so unfair!

I spent the morning classes in a dismal funk, even *after* I'd heard that the principal had ordered the Student Body to go home to change into "decent" clothes. Nobody could understand why she was so meek about agreeing to do it. But then, while we were all in the cafeteria, she turned up on the lunch line wearing a veil and covered from head to toe in the black robes of a nun! The place went into an uproar, with hundreds of cheering kids stomping on the floor. Then the "nun" jumped up on a tabletop to do something like a Dance of the Seven Veils.

"Come on, everybody, do your thing!" she called out. Soon almost all the guys and at least half the girls were up on the tabletops themselves, either yowling and rain dancing like Hollywood-style Indians or doing their own versions of the Macarena.

As a demonstration of sticking up for freedom of expression, this was great; as a demonstration of how far the Student Body would go to hog all the attention for herself, it was pretty pathetic. On my bus ride home I began to daydream what Alicia would do to make me popular. It would have to be very cool and sophisticated without giving anybody the slightest chance of thinking that I was showing off.

Yeah, well, that was all nothing but make-believe. Meanwhile, I was that same zitzy little mouse who'd already turned down the one chance I'd had! I took a halfhearted look at my side window. Nothing, of course. Later, while getting off, I took a quick glance at the driver's mirror. Just me again, and I told myself I should be glad of it. What was I trying to get myself into? Did I really want to risk going completely insane?

Still, I went into my house half hoping to see Alicia gliding along beside me to the closet. She wasn't there. Again I told myself to stop playing with fire. "Anyone home?" I called out. When no one answered, I went straight to my room and threw myself facedown on the bed.

How long did I lie there stewing about not having a life? Maybe an hour, because the house was getting dim when I heard a little *click* that sounded as if the medicine cabinet had just opened by itself. I lifted my head and looked toward the bathroom that adjoined my room. The medicine cabinet door was swinging slowly out over the washbasin. It stopped when the mirror was facing straight into my room. I didn't have to guess whose image would be in it when I jumped to my feet. Alicia was beckoning to me. As I walked toward the mirror, she said, "You hurt me pretty badly, you know."

"I'm sorry."

She was silent for a while. Then she asked, "Do you really mean that?"

"I never like to hurt anyone," I said.

She lifted her eyes. "I'm just anyone?"

"I didn't mean it that way."

"Look, just tell me if you want me to help you. Because if you don't—"

"But I do!"

"All right then." She brightened a little and said, "It's gloomy in here. Why don't you put on the light?"

"Just tell me one thing. Are you just in my mind?

40

A hallucination?" I asked as I flicked the switch.

"Would it make a difference?"

"I . . . I don't know."

"No, Alice," she said firmly. "I exist now. I'm a separate being from you. And you shouldn't be unhappy about that, because if I weren't, I wouldn't be able to do as much for you as I want to do. I love you, Alice. You gave me a chance to come alive. I want to make you feel comfortable about it and not so wary of me that I can't be of any use to you. Because if you are, then what's the *point?* Do you see what I'm saying?"

"I guess so," I told her, feeling kind of dazed.

"Well, you don't seem very convinced," Alicia sighed, "but I guess it's where we'll have to start. Could you do me a favor and get hold of a little mirror you could keep with you and open anywhere, so we don't have to keep getting together on bus windows and clock faces and all that? It's tiring and it's catch-as-catch-can. I'd rather have a more dependable way of communicating."

"I suppose I could borrow one of my mother's compacts."

Alicia frowned. "When you say *borrow* . . ."

"I wouldn't tell her anything. She has extras and she wouldn't even notice."

"Good." Alicia paused, then said, "That brings up something that I feel a bit . . . awkward about raising."

"What?"

"If I'm going to help you, it has to be a complete secret from *everybody*." She had lowered her eyes while saying it, but now she looked straight into mine.

"About my parents and everyone else, that's okay. I wouldn't want them to know anyway. But I don't have secrets from Wendy. She's my best friend. That doesn't mean I don't value you, too," I added hastily.

Alicia was silent again. Then she shook her head. "I'm sorry, but it can't work that way. So perhaps I'd better just leave now."

Suddenly she vanished, and once again I saw not even myself.

"Wait a minute!" I cried. "Can't we talk about this?"

I heard her voice coming from the mirror, but there was no image to go with it. "I'm sorry, Alice. I appreciate your position, I really do. But your request is just making it too painful for both of us."

"Tell me why!"

"Because Wendy would try to put a stop to it. Do I really have to say more than that? I'm not somebody who wants to be in a fight, Alice. For one thing, I'm much too vulnerable. What's more, I wouldn't even be able to help you if you kept going back and forth in your mind about whether to give our arrangement a chance or not. No, no. Here's what I can do. Let's try it for a few weeks. After that you can quit. If you do, then that will be it for me, and I'll go back to being your ordinary image. But you have to give me some time to make things work for you."

"You want me to lie to Wendy?"

"I'm not telling you to lie. Just don't say anything about me."

"But what if she asks me if I'm spending time with you?"

"All I can say is that the very minute you tell her about me, I'll be gone."

"Oh, this is so hard!" I exclaimed.

"For me, too, because you don't trust me," she said, and I could hear her sadness.

"But that's not saying anything against you, Alicia. Trust is something that has to be built."

There was another pause before I heard her say in an uncertain tone, "Is that right? Well, I suppose it might be so. There are things that I have to learn, too, Alice. I can't see everything just from living on the surface."

"Then we can help each other," I said.

"Still, I need your promise that you won't say anything or let Wendy find out anything until I tell you I feel secure about it. That's fair, isn't it?"

"I suppose it is. But if I have to lie to her, then I don't know . . ."

Her voice grew harder. "Can you tell me you know

anyone who never tells lies, not for any reason?"

"No, I can't say that. But I never lie to my best friend."

There was a long pause. Finally, Alicia said, "Can't you tell yourself that you're only *postponing the time* when you're going to tell her?"

"I . . . I guess so," I said.

"It's a deal!" she cried, brightening suddenly into view. "And here's how we seal the promise. Put your hands against the mirror, like this."

Slowly I brought my hands up against the place where she was pressing hers. But as soon as I touched the glass, I felt such a pang inside that I almost yanked my hands away.

"Done!" she exclaimed, before I could say anything about changing my mind. The bargain was made, and there was such happiness dancing in her eyes that I just couldn't go back on it.

Chapter 4

Alicia felt that the best place for me to learn how to dress and carry myself wasn't where I was living—which she called "the boonies"—but in New York City. It was no problem at all to get my mom to take me there on Saturday. She'd been after me for a year or more to make a mother-and-daughter day out of going to the city on a shopping spree.

I had never wanted to go because I had awful memories of being taken there when I was small to see the Macy's Thanksgiving Day Parade and then somehow getting separated from my parents. As I ran around trying to find them, a very tall person I was afraid of lifted me high over the crowd like I was one of the balloons until my mother saw me!

The next time I got talked into going, there was all this *noise* that wouldn't let up, from the second we got out of the train station: police sirens, and horns honking as cabs zigzagged in front of each other so fast they looked like they would crash, and jackhammers tearing up the streets.

Anyway, my mom could never get me to go on one of those "let's do the town together, you and I" trips. Now, Alicia was pushing me to do it. Since I wasn't going to be seeing Wendy, I gave in—and made sure to be standing in front of the shiny glass-front cabinet where we kept all our good china while I amazed my mom by telling her how much I'd just love to go with her to the city the next day.

My mother is the kind of person who always feels more comfortable when a suggestion comes from her. That's because, unless she's already set for it, something in her automatically causes her to back off and look for what's wrong with the idea. This is exactly what she did (as maybe I secretly hoped she would) when I suggested the shopping trip.

Yes, a trip to New York was something she had always wanted to do with me, she began . . . if only I'd asked her before she had volunteered to make a visit tomorrow to the AIDS babies at St. Jude's Hospital. Couldn't we do it next Saturday?

Well, I was happy enough to get a reprieve from going. Alicia, reflecting from the cabinet behind my mother, shook her head with such a suspicious look that my face must have fallen by a mile.

Right away my mother said, "Oh, poor baby! Does it really mean that much to you to go tomorrow? Well, of course it does. What am I thinking? It's just terrible that you can't see Wendy. I won't say a word about her mother, but she is so-o-o rigid! Well, I'm certainly not going to be rigid about this myself. Let me just make a call or two and see if I can switch some things around."

"I don't think I should keep you from those AIDS babies!" I blurted.

"Nonsense! Marianne Feeny and I switch all the time."

Before nine the next morning we were on a train, and by ten-thirty Mom and I were roaming the halls of the Museum of Modern Art—a diversion that was meant to inspire me to embrace the idea of shopping. I tried to let Alicia look at the paintings, too, by flashing open the compact that I kept in my palm.

"Look at that one!" Alicia said to me, so I stopped by a beautiful picture of dancers. When my mother had walked on a bit, I whispered, "Yes, it's lovely."

"Who's talking about anything on the walls!" she declared impatiently. "Concentrate on what we're here for. That woman over there—look how she moves. The way she's got her head tilted as she stands in front of that crazy-looking statue, stepping back from it and then closer in, as if she really understands what it's about, though she probably doesn't have any more idea than I do. I'll tell you what she does know about though. How to carry her hip just a little bit higher on one side. See how that gives her other side an elegant curved line? It's like *she's* the real work of art in this place—and that guy knows it."

"What guy?"

"The one across the room who looks like he's about to drop dead over her."

I was kind of shocked. "You mean that she wants to . . . to pick him up?"

"Probably not. My guess is she just wants to know that she *could*. See, she's walking away. Look how she's going down the stairs with one hand just lightly touching the rail, trailing along so it catches your eye. It makes her the center of everything. Even the guard is looking at her. She isn't that beautiful, but she carries herself like she is. Did you see how she had her face made up?"

"Alicia! That woman's at least ten or fifteen years older than me!" I said. "I'm not interested in attracting some older guy. David DeWitt is good enough for me."

"Really, Alice, grown men are far more interesting," Alicia said.

"Listen to me, please!" I blurted. "I know you're more sophisticated than I am. But I'm not in a hurry to grow up that fast. And if you want to make me feel safe with you, don't push me. I'm only fifteen years old!"

"Alice, why are you talking to yourself?"

"Huh?"

Snapping the compact closed, I spun around to face my mother. I must have raised my voice too loudly.

"I heard you doing it yesterday in your room, too," she said, giving me a very worried look.

"I . . . uh . . . I guess some thoughts got into my mind, and without realizing it I said them out loud."

"You never used to do that," my mom replied.

"Well . . . uh . . . there are lots of things I've never done before." I imitated one of Alicia's airy smiles. For good measure I tossed my head.

My mother stared at me closely for a minute, then came to some kind of decision. "As long as we're here, I'm going to call Maurice's Salon and try to get you an appointment for today, even if I have to get down on my knees and beg for it."

"An appointment for what?" I asked with trepidation.

"To get that hair out of your eyes and off your face. I just can't stand it anymore, living with a shaggy . . . person."

Of course, I knew she was about to call me a dog, but I let it go. Meanwhile, Alicia had been watching from a shiny brass picture frame. As soon as my mother had gone downstairs to find a phone booth, I opened my compact. Alicia was ready with a comment.

"Hooray!"

"I am not going to let all my pimples show!"

"Don't chicken out on me. It wastes my precious energies. Your mom's instincts are right."

"New York is so expensive. I can't ask her to spend that kind of money!"

"Now listen. I've been studying you and your mom for a long time. She never knows what to do for you, and this is her chance. You *owe* it to her to accept with a gracious smile! Are you listening?"

I nodded moodily.

"You should get a perm. But don't just *ask* for one. Make her come up with that idea herself. Okay?"

"I guess."

Alicia waggled a finger at me. "And remember. One way or another I'll be watching to see if you sabotage my plan."

"And what happens to me if I mess up?" I demanded. "Is there a prison where mirrors lock up disobedient people?"

She grinned at me. "Now that's a thought."

My mom came back overjoyed. Since there was a virus going around, three people had canceled their appointments. I was slotted in with somebody called Miss Bernice, provided we could get there in less than fifteen minutes. We dashed over to Avenue of the Americas, then ran, huffing and puffing, a bunch of blocks to Rockefeller Center—and promptly got lost. After many wrong turns in the underground maze of shops, we finally found Maurice's and practically fell through the door, exhausted.

Maurice's Salon was like a tranquil island. I hated it immediately. I hated the smell of perfume. I hated the music, which had no beat to it at all. What was I getting myself into? Did Alicia have the same idea of "up-to-date" as my mother did—something from the early Colonial era?

Then the star of one of the daytime soaps walked past me. Suddenly, she turned to where I was sitting, bent down until we were almost face-to-face, and said, "You know, I had a case just like that. Best thing that ever happened to me, because it got me a walk-on role as the sister of a gang member. The money I made paid for my membership in the Screen Actors' Guild, and I've been working ever since."

She actually gave me a combination head toss and smile like Alicia's, then walked out, leaving me to wonder why I had been picked to listen to that speech. But my mother, who had been grinning through it like a loon, said it was "inspirational."

Well, to make a long story short, Miss Bernice, who was very slim and sexy, asked me what I wanted, and I shrugged. Then she asked my mother what she wanted. My mother, who is usually quite decisive, mumbled in confusion for a while, waved her hand in a circle around her ear, then gave up and said, "Just to look nice."

Finally Miss Bernice suggested, "How about you leave it all to me?"

It was one of those moments of truth. My mom was frowning, and I could tell she was thinking about what she could say to my dad if everything cost too much. I glanced into the mirror, where Alicia, after looking Miss Bernice up and down, was nodding. Then she shot me another you-better-not-sabotage-this look. "Mom, I don't want you to spend a lot of money," I said quickly.

"Shoot the works!" my mother cried.

That's how my hair got to be dyed flaming red, trimmed, and permed, with my long bangs swept back. My nails were even manicured.

"I can't believe this is you!" my mother sang as we left.

"You keep saying that," I told her. "And I know why, too."

"Why?" Again that worried look.

"Because you'll have to explain to Daddy that you sank over a hundred dollars."

"A *hundred?* You're not even close. Let's not talk about your father." She slipped her arm into mine. "We'd better enjoy this day, because we may not have another!"

Before we finished, we had visited the most expensive stores. Bloomingdales was the biggest temptation, because we went there first just to "look around."

Alicia was going nuts. I could see her in hundreds of mirrors and glass display cases, holding her nose at all the sweaters and things I liked.

"What's bothering you?" my mom asked at last.

"Nothing. This is great!" I said.

"I know, you want to look at all the stuff we can't afford," she muttered unhappily.

"No, I don't."

I glanced at Alicia. As soon as I saw that she approved of what I was saying, I switched it around. "Yes, Mom," I said, "I do want to see what they've got. And I don't just want to *look* at it. I want you to buy it for me. I want to change my life. And I think I'm worth every cent."

Now that really ticked Alicia off, and for a moment I thought she might even vanish. But too much was too much! My family was not made of money, and I wasn't going to let some image in a mirror make us bankrupt.

My mother, meanwhile, had nearly gone into a state of shock. But then she said, "Well, I was going to spend money on you at Christmas. I suppose we could spend some of it now."

This was a complete turnaround, and I couldn't believe it. We went to one of the more expensive departments, and right away Mom started pulling out her credit card. Of course, little did she know that it was greedy Alicia who did the selecting. She would spot something from a distance and keep jabbing her finger at it until my mother and I had to drop everything and go flying at her beck and call. My poor dazed mother kept saying, "Well, if you really like it. . . ." I wound up with a dress, a cashmere sweater, some blouses, and two skirts before Alicia catapulted us to the accessories, where I got a belt and a purple silk scarf—which Alicia modeled for me in the mirror—to set off my hair.

"My goodness, what have we unleashed here?" my amazed mother gasped as we careened down Fifth Avenue to Lord & Taylor. "You certainly seem to have discovered that the key to New York is a foolish woman flashing her credit card."

"Mom, I told you I don't want you to spend any more!" I insisted, since my mother had changed her psychology.

"Nonsense," she said, reverting suddenly to her usual contrary ways. "If this is an investment in your happiness, I'm glad to make it."

"I've got some money saved from my birthday to throw in," I offered lamely.

Mom eyed me hungrily. "How much?"

"A hundred and ten dollars."

"Not enough, but I'll take it!" She stared at my feet. "You need shoes."

"*Everybody* wears sneakers," I pleaded.

But Alicia shook her head at me from a store window. She was very firm about what she wanted. And since I didn't have a clue of my own, I felt that I had to go along.

Chapter 5

I was beginning to have second thoughts about Alicia becoming such a big part of my life so quickly. Plenty of them. But she was always so *convincing*. She had a good reason for everything she insisted I do, like wearing what she picked out for me. She even persuaded me to use eyeshadow, lipstick, and powder.

"You just have to put it all on very lightly," she said, "so you don't draw attention to any of it. It should almost not be there. If you do it right, the guys only notice the *effect*."

In fact, we spent all day Sunday experimenting with different "faces" for me. There was the "wholesome and innocent look," which she didn't like at all. And "dangerous to men," which I hated. And, finally, "just a bit naughty but not too adventurous," which we agreed to try.

Monday morning I was up an hour early to go through my new makeup routine. It sure was worth the loss of sleep. From the moment I stepped onto the bus, people were looking at me as if they didn't know me. I almost didn't know myself. I felt so different—even with all my pimples—that this time I sat down in *front* of David DeWitt. If somebody was going to shoot secret glances at anybody, let him do it to me!

Of course, I didn't really expect him to, not after seeing him on Friday with the Student Body. Yet as everybody got off the bus, he did give me a friendly nod as he walked past me on those long legs of his. Well, I had long legs of my own, and I used them to hurry down to the lockers so I could see Wendy and talk over her mother's law against our getting together. Also I wanted to find out how she was—and, without giving anything away about Alicia, to see what she thought about my new look!

But I didn't find her there. Was her leg still so bad that she'd been kept home? I asked a girl who knew her, and she said Wendy had come in on crutches and gone off to her homeroom. Without waiting to see me? That made me feel awful!

I went to my own homeroom, where I moped around until the loudspeaker crackled. Mr. Perlmutter, the principal, spoke in a coldly furious voice: "Last week there was a disgraceful incident in the cafeteria, and I have had the weekend to decide what to do about it. As a rule, I would not wish to punish everyone for the actions of some. But in this instance it appears that a very large number of students participated in an uncontrolled display of childish behavior that caused destruction to school property. I have therefore decided to cancel this year's theatrical production of *Hair*. Any further such outbreaks will be met with expulsions. I want you all to know that I do not say this in anger but for your own good!"

That certainly woke me up—and everyone else around me. We were all outraged as we headed off to our first classes. Luckily, I had Social Studies, and Mr. Simms let the students who felt like it sound off.

Even with my new look, I was reluctant to join in. I held back to see if others would say what I was feeling so I wouldn't have to speak up. Alicia, who'd been staring up at me from the open compact on my lap, kept shaking her head as if she couldn't believe I wasn't taking part.

I felt such pressure from her to do something that I made the most terrible choice in the world. I called out, "Mr. Simms, I'd really like to hear what *you* think about it."

Everybody grew real quiet while he cleared his throat. "I don't think I should express an opinion," he began slowly, "because my role is to encourage all of you to think and speak for yourselves. And now that the class has had a chance to blow off steam, I'd like to hear some calm and reasonable discussion. Would you care to begin, Alice?"

Snapping the compact shut, I hesitated. "I . . . uh . . . uh . . ."

I just sat there feeling shaky. While I was still

getting myself together so I could talk, a boy behind me raised his voice in disgust and said, "Mr. Simms, I never thought *you'd* be afraid to speak up."

"Well, I'm sorry that you think I am," the teacher replied huskily. I could tell his feelings were hurt.

By then I could sense Alicia's eyes burning into me from the glass-enclosed bulletin board. I guess she wanted me to defend Mr. Simms. Everybody was already yelling back and forth at once, taking sides.

The arguing went on until the bell. When I went to Signing, I saw Wendy in her seat with her crutches against a wall. There was an expression on her face that I couldn't figure out as she watched me cross the room. As soon as I got to my place, she made the love sign, which I really needed just then!

Unfortunately, the teacher wanted us to pick new signing partners, so we didn't get to do much else until just before the period ended. Then Wendy signaled me that I looked great. That made me happy, and I let her know it. But she frowned and made a question mark with her right hand and spelled out the word *Alicia*. She wanted to know if my "hallucination" had anything to do with this.

"Don't call her that!" I signaled back.

"Why, Alice? Does this Alicia understand sign language, too?"

I don't know whether I was mad at Wendy or scared of Alicia or both. But I was certainly uncomfortable.

"I don't know," I wrote in the air. "Let's stop talking!" And we each looked the other way.

I won't go into how the rest of the school day passed, except that it was a mix between feeling good over getting some friendly compliments and feeling bad about Wendy and what had happened in Social Studies. From about one o'clock on, rumors that Mr. Simms had gotten himself into trouble started flying. I didn't know much more than that until I went to Study Hall, the next-to-the-last class for the day. The news was horrible.

During his lunch break, Mr. Simms had told some of the other teachers in the lounge that, in his opinion, the principal was creating a problem with the students that didn't have to exist. He also said that if he didn't find a graceful way to back off from canceling the play, things could get out of control.

It seems that someone overheard this and told the principal, maybe putting a nasty spin on it. Mr. Perlmutter apparently got furious and told Mr. Simms he would be replaced by a substitute teacher as of the following Monday.

I felt that this was all my fault. If only I hadn't put Mr. Simms on the spot in front of the class, maybe he would have kept his thoughts to himself and not gotten into so much trouble! He was probably the best teacher in the school, and now I had ruined his career.

When the last class of the day ended and we were ready to go home, members of the Student Council were shouting in the hallways that there'd be an emergency meeting the following day at lunchtime in the auditorium—and all the students were supposed to be there.

On the bus going home, I made up my mind to speak out at that meeting and call for a student strike until Mr. Simms's punishment for exercising his right of free speech was revoked. I thought this issue was even more important than the school play, because it had to do with a person's life and career and the chance to earn a living at what he did best.

Since I knew how awfully easy it was for me to imagine being brave without really acting courageously, I decided to write down what I had to say. After repeating it over and over at home, I would be less likely to choke up when it had to be done for real.

By the time I got off the bus, my speech was written. The words had come pouring out of me! Alicia was so proud of me that as soon as we got home, she helped me rehearse until I had perfected my presentation. She even gave me pointers on how to walk up to the platform and then just stand there waiting until everyone was silent.

"If you go up looking nervous," she said, "then you're just another worked-up person taking a turn.

Everyone will fidget and scratch because you're fidgeting and scratching. The audience will forget half of what you've said before you walk away. Instead, you want to be so much in control of yourself that they'll feel you're speaking for them, only better. You understand, Alice?"

"Yes," I said.

"Okay. Now let's go over it from the second you get up from your seat: how you walk to the platform, how you lift your head and look all around the audience before you speak, what you do with your arms. Then, when we're all done with that, let's pick out your clothes and decide on your look. I think it should be simple, no nonsense, and direct."

Breaking into a smile, Alicia added, "And you can give hints here and there of how very feminine you can be. Don't you think so?"

"I . . . I guess."

"Good!"

The auditorium had a high ceiling and lots of tall windows on one side. So when the students crowded into the place, Alicia had no problem reflecting me from all sorts of shiny surfaces while I turned into one of the rows to find a seat. I took one on the side aisle very close to the back. As soon as I opened the compact, Alicia looked up at me with a worried expression. We had agreed that I would try to be one

61

of the first people inside so I could sit up front and have a good chance of being called on.

Why hadn't I done that? All I know is that before I entered the auditorium, my throat was so dry that I desperately needed water. There was a line in front of the fountain, so I waited. Of course I could have run to the sink in the girls' bathroom, but then I would have had Alicia yelling at me from the mirror.

Anyway, from the seat I finally got I could still call out to be recognized. At least that's what I told myself while David DeWitt, as Student Council president, opened the meeting. His speech was mostly about the show, not the Social Studies teacher. Then some other members of the council spoke. Finally, it was time for those of us in the audience to raise our hands.

This was my chance, but even though I had gulped a gallon of water, my throat had dried out like a desert again. I also felt a hop-hopping in my chest, like a car engine misfiring.

All of a sudden, I had a blinding vision of Alicia jumping! How can I explain it? It was like she was leaping right out from that tiny mirror. A wave hit me and rolled right over me the way an ocean wave knocks someone off a surfboard. Only this wasn't a wall of water. It was a wall of energy.

That energy wave carried me off. All at once I was traveling through a darkness so thick that I felt it close around and behind me as I passed through. In that trembling blackness, I heard murmuring, buzzing, voicelike noises coming closer and closer. Then I felt sticky things touch me. I couldn't see anything, although my eyes opened as far as they could go. My skin crawled at the sensation of spidery oozes stuck all over me. I couldn't shake them off.

All I could do was press my way blindly through, until suddenly I burst out into the light. Light was streaming from behind me—and *through* me!

Where was I, now that I'd left that terrifying nothingness? Where had that wave carried me? To one of those big tall windows in the auditorium. Was I *in front* of the window? Oh, no. Nothing like that. I was on it! Alicia's wave of energy had turned me into a mirror image!

Alicia jumped up from my seat to walk toward the platform. "Listen, everybody!" she called out as if she owned the place. "I want to speak about what happened to one of the finest people in this school, Mr. Simms!"

A tremendous roar filled the room, especially from the kids who'd been in Mr. Simms's class with me. Alicia stepped onto the stage looking perfect and radiant—not a single zit anywhere on *that* face!—and then she delivered *my* speech!

Not that I heard the first part of it. How could I? From the sides of my window came pitiful moaning cries of *things* that seemed to plead with me to bring them out of the blackness and into the light.

I don't know what it was that made me fling this answering thought at them: "Leave me alone. I am *not* Alicia!"

The murmurings from the sides grew strangely hesitant, then stopped. It seemed as if the things out there in nothingness were falling back because they had become afraid of me.

In the auditorium, Alicia's speech had such a terrific effect that the kids jumped to their feet, applauding madly and shouting for a student strike. As Alicia started to walk back toward her seat, Wendy stood up and threw her arms around her.

Despite being way up on the window, I heard Wendy say, "Oh, Alice, you were so wonderful! You did it! You broke though all your shyness and it was beautiful!"

I heard this for the same reason that I suddenly began feeling Wendy's embrace. How it happened, I don't know, but I had just come back into my own body! It was *me* that hundreds of people were yelling and cheering for.

I was very shaken and confused—and then I saw Alicia. She was only inches away from my face, glinting at me from the thick lenses of Wendy's glasses and telling me with a smile, "Look, Alice, how popular I've made you! Aren't you proud of me?"

Wendy couldn't hear her, but she certainly heard me cry out, "You had no right to do that to me!"

Wendy pulled back, startled. "What?"

"I . . . I didn't mean you!" I stammered.

"Oh, no, you didn't mean *her*," snapped Alicia. "She's such a great and fantastic friend. Yet she's never done a thing for you, while I just put the whole school at your feet!"

I couldn't take this anymore. I was so overwhelmed that I hurried from the auditorium, grabbed my coat, and left the building. Then I walked—I don't know how many miles, four, five, six, or seven—all the way home, trying to clear my mind.

Chapter 6

I think that Alicia knew better than to come near me during that walk. I was still a live volcano as I entered my house. She came floating up to me on the hallway mirror, apologizing for taking my place so forcibly. "I only meant it for the best," she said.

First I made sure nobody else was home. Then I let her have it. "That blackness is horrible," I said. "Horrible."

"Yes, I know. It's what I had to fight my way out of in order to become your mirror image. I'm sorry I had to put you through it, but it was for your own good."

"But you didn't get my permission first!"

"Alice, I *couldn't*! I didn't even know it was happening myself. I was just feeling so frustrated that, after all the rehearsing and planning, you simply sat there like a lump. The next thing I knew, I was going up to the stage myself and doing it *for* you. I have no idea how I sprang into your place. It surprised me as much as it did you. Please believe me."

"All right, maybe that makes me less angry at you. But that still doesn't—"

She cut me off, saying, "Look, Alice, I can't help

thinking maybe you gave me the energy for that to happen. Maybe you wanted it."

"No, I didn't," I barked at her.

"Be honest. Are you *completely* sure?"

Alicia stared at me as if she could look right through me. And suddenly I lost all my confidence. "I don't know," I said shakily. "Maybe I did without realizing it. But, Alicia, it was very scary!"

She nodded, and her face softened into such sadness that I thought she might cry. "I'm so sorry," she whispered. "I really am. But please, just tell me, don't you think I did well?"

There was such a hunger for forgiveness in her voice that I couldn't hold it back. "You promise never to take my place again?"

"Yes, of course. But like I said, Alice, I wasn't aware."

"Well, I want you to be aware. I'm asking you to never do it again."

"I'll be very careful."

"Careful is not enough. Just don't do it!"

"I won't—unless you ask me to, of course," Alicia added slyly.

"*That*, believe me, is not going to happen. Either change the subject or shut up."

Alicia nodded and seemed to hold back a sigh. Then she said, "You didn't tell me what you thought about the speech."

"I didn't hear most of it," I told her. "But I could see that you were doing great. I only wish it could have been me."

"Next time it will be you!" she cried, lighting up like a bonfire. "You'll do all sorts of fabulous things, Alice! Just see if you don't. You only needed to have a demonstration, that's all."

"I guess you're right," I said uncertainly. Then I frowned again. "But I didn't like the way you looked and sounded when Wendy stood up to congratulate you. She's my best friend and has been for years and years."

"How did I look and sound?" Alicia asked in a bewildered tone.

"Jealous of her."

Sparks seemed to shoot out of her eyes. "I was *not* jealous!"

"No? Well, you certainly could have fooled me."

"In my opinion, Wendy was jealous of you. Oh, she knew how to hide it, all right, but I saw through it. And you don't need that, Alice. You've outgrown her."

"That's for me to say, not you!" I screamed at her. "So back off!"

"Well, I guess I'd better, since it seems like now I can't do anything right."

"Stop it. I can't handle any more of this!" I buried my face in my hands. "Maybe *you* don't know the shock you gave me by changing places, but my head's been ringing like a bell since it happened."

"Oh, I'm so sorry about that," she exclaimed. "Listen, why don't you hang up our coat, and let's go upstairs so you can lie down?"

"It's not *our* coat," I muttered. "It's *my* coat. But lying down is a good idea."

I was anxious to get rid of her, and once I got to the bedroom, my headache was the excuse I used to pull down the window shades. That cut off any light falling on the glassy picture frames on my dresser. Luckily I had never gotten around to hanging up a mirror in the bedroom! One mirror to reflect my zitface was enough. Then I sneaked along a wall to close the bathroom door, making sure that the mirror over the sink wouldn't reflect my arm.

I checked the clock. Wendy would be home by now. Getting into bed and taking the phone with me under the covers, I felt around for the right buttons and prayed that Wendy—not her mother—would answer.

I was lucky. "It's me," I whispered. "Wendy, listen. That wasn't me who was up on the stage. It was *Alicia!* I know it sounds incredible, but she found a way to trade places with me!"

The long silence that followed made it absolutely clear that she didn't believe me. "All right," I said, "I don't blame you for thinking that I'm losing my mind. But I'm telling you the truth! How can I—?"

"Alice," she cut in, but then didn't seem able to follow up with anything else except, "I'm so worried about you."

"Wait a minute!" I blurted. "I know how to prove this! While I was giving that speech, did you see one single zit on my face?"

"There was no way for me to tell," she answered. "You were too far away from where I was sitting. I didn't get a real good look at you until I got up to say how great you were. And there were pimples on your face then, Alice."

"But, Wendy," I cried in frustration, "that was *after* Alicia went up there and did her thing. By the time you hugged me, she'd switched back with me! Can't you please believe me?"

"Alice, I'm asking you to listen! You did something so marvelous today that now you can't even allow yourself to accept that it was you. I think we've got to get you to a doctor who *knows* about people who don't feel that they deserve—"

"You're wrong! You're wrong! You won't listen, and there isn't any doctor for this."

"Then we'll go to church and ask Father Francis to find you an exorcist. You know, like in that old movie."

"First you said Alicia was a hallucination, now she's a demon. But neither is true."

"No? Then what is she?"

"Someone that my own energy brought to life."

"I never heard of anything like that," said Wendy as gently as she could. "And you know, you're not the first person in the world whose mind got fixed on something that . . . well . . . what I'm trying to say is, somebody doesn't have to be crazy to—"

Desperately I cut in. "Didn't you see all the changes I made in just a few days? My new clothes and my appearance?"

"*You* made them, Alice. Be proud of it! Accept it."

Suddenly there was a sharp rap on my bedroom door, and my mother, who was always polite enough to knock but too impatient to wait for an answer, walked in. "What in the world are you doing lying there in the dark? Are you sick?" she asked.

"Just a bad headache, Mom."

"I'll get you a couple of aspirins," she said, marching to the bathroom and throwing on the light. She yanked open the medicine cabinet, not knowing, of course, that it brought Alicia swinging out in search of me.

"I don't need any. I'll be all right," I told her.

"Here they are!" Leaving the cabinet-door mirror still facing my bed, she came back with the pills and a glass of water. "Sit up now. Why have you got the phone under the sheets? Talking to Wendy, I'll bet. That's just what you two used to do when you were children. Let me speak to her."

There was nothing I could do but give her the receiver. "Hello, darling. How are you feeling? Is your leg any better? Oh, that's good. Listen, dear, is your mother home? I'd like to speak to her. No? Well, has she said anything about you and Alice being friends again? You think it'll be all right with her? Good. Give her my best regards. And come to dinner as soon as you can. Alice has been so lost without you, and I miss you, too. You were always just like one of my own. Do you want Alice back? Oh, you have to get off now. All right, you'll talk later. 'Bye."

My mother handed me the receiver as she bustled past me, saying, "I'll bring your dinner upstairs to you."

"No, Mom, I'll come downstairs with you!" I cried, without glancing at the bathroom mirror.

But as I hurried out of the room, I heard Alicia calling after me, "It was very foolish of you to try to convince Wendy. Don't you see that if she did believe you, it would make a lot more trouble for us? Alice, come back and talk to me about it. Alice!"

I didn't escape her by going downstairs to the kitchen. Alicia's face frowned up at me from the bottom of my water glass. I even saw a brooding image of her in my teaspoon. That made me so jumpy that the spoon fell out of my hand when the phone rang. For some crazy reason I had the notion that it was Alicia calling me.

My mother spoke to the caller and turned to me. "It's for you," she said. "Someone named Dave DeWitt."

My mouth dropped open. She gave me a knowing little smile, covered the phone, and said, "He sounds cute."

When I took the phone, David said, "Hi. You went off so fast, I didn't get a chance to talk to you after the meeting. I wanted to tell you how right you were about making Mr. Simms our first priority. The committee is ready to call a sitdown strike. What do you think?"

"I'm not exactly sure what you mean," I mumbled.

"Well, instead of nobody showing up, we all show up and go to our classes. This proves we're not just taking advantage of an issue to cut school."

"What do we do in class?"

"We sit there, but we don't do anything. No quiz-taking, no handing in homework, no answering study questions. And listen, what would you say to everybody wearing gags to protest what's being done to our freedom of speech?"

"David, that's great!"

"Call me Davy," he said. "My real friends do."

"Okay . . . Davy."

"So you like that part of it, huh?"

"I do."

"It was my idea," he said proudly.

"Well, it's really good." Then I added, "Maybe we can get the newspaper to cover it."

"Oh, yeah, well, it'll be in the *Roll Call*."

"No, I don't mean just the school paper."

"Hey, you're right! I'll take care of it. Listen, you know that coffee shop in town, the Espresso? It's Open Mike night tomorrow, and my band's going to be playing."

"Oh, I didn't know you had one."

"Yeah, we just formed the group. We're only playing on Wednesdays, for no money, but some of the guys have already done some professional stuff—backup recording, things like that. We've been practicing in a garage, but you need an audience to get a sense of what you're doing."

"Absolutely!" I agreed. My mother turned around to give me a know-it-all stare.

"So you want to come?"

"You mean . . ." I had to stop to take a breath. "With you?"

"Sure. Yeah. Of course."

"I thought you were seeing—"

"She's just a friend," he said quickly.

"That's all? But everybody thinks—"

"That's the whole point! She's got to have an audience watching everything she does. Everything's got to be a performance, you know what I mean?"

"How do you know that I'm not like that?"

75

There was a silence. "First of all, because you've got a brain. That's in addition to looking great."

I caught my breath. "You . . . think I look . . . great?"

It was stupid of me to repeat that aloud, because before I could cover the phone, my mother giggled and started clapping her hands. I could have killed her!

"Well, yeah," Davy said. "That's what I mean about you not being all filled up with yourself. You don't even know how people see you."

"But I haven't always looked so—" In half a second flat my mother was at my side, jabbing me hard on the shoulder to make me shut up.

"Well, you sure have changed," he declared enthusiastically. "So I'll see you tomorrow night?"

I was having some very mixed feelings by now. Still I said, "Yes, I'd like it."

"Great. Want to meet me there? I'd come for you only I don't have wheels."

"No, that's all right," I told him, though I was already getting a strange heavy feeling in my chest. "What time?"

"Well, it starts about eight-thirty, and we'll be setting up our equipment before that. The session will run about an hour, and we can hang out after."

"That late?" I said, already feeling my face start to burn. "I don't know if my mother—"

"You can make it!" she snapped.

"Hey, sounds like you got somebody on my side over there!"

"My mom watches heartwarming movies and reads romance novels with the covers torn off," I said, ducking away from her shove and laughing. "Anyway, I'll see you on the bus tomorrow."

"No, I'm getting in early with the rest of the council to organize the strike as people come in before the first bell. Don't forget to bring your gag. Well, see you."

"Okay. Right." I hung up. "Mom, why couldn't you behave?"

"Because I am so thrilled for you!" She stared at me. "What's the matter with you, Alice? You don't seem to be happy at all."

"Why should I be happy?" I snapped. "It's not *me* he's interested in."

"No? Who is it then?"

"You'd never understand!"

That hurt her. "Why don't you just try to explain?"

"I can't. I can't. I *can't*."

"Alice, stop it. You're getting red in the face."

Red? Yes, I supposed so. Because I was feeling as if a volcano was erupting under the surface of my face. Molten lava was bubbling up. Lava that would push through as pimples, pimples that would blister and burst.

David DeWitt had made his date with Alice, but it was Alicia he wanted. He just didn't know it yet. He wouldn't know until tomorrow when the sitdown strike started and everybody would see *Miss Zits* stuffing a gag in her mouth!

Chapter 7

The medicine-cabinet mirror was still jutting out over the sink when I walked into my room. "So what are you going to do about that date?" Alicia called through the open door.

"You're everywhere I go, aren't you?"

"Why wouldn't I be? I'm your reflection."

"Lucky me," I growled, ready to explode with frustration. I stomped into the bathroom to take it out on her. "Just how long do you intend to keep getting involved in my life?"

She matched my jumpiness with her cool manner. "How long will you need me?"

"I didn't say that I needed you at all."

"Are you really going to go out like that tomorrow night with your face so inflamed and breaking out?" she asked.

"Why?" I demanded, staring her down. "Are you volunteering to take my place again?"

"Not if you don't want it."

"Well, I don't!"

"No problem then," she said, starting to yawn. "Listen, you'll have to excuse me." I saw her turn away in the mirror and walk out of the bathroom stretching her arms. Then she flopped down on my bed! It was all so real that I even heard the springs mash down. That gave me a scare. "Get off there!" I yelled.

"Just trying to get the feel of being in a bed, but I still can't," she sighed. "I can put myself here but can't really touch anything. It's all so near and yet so far, if you know what I mean. It always looked so wonderful when I watched you lying down, growing so cozy and dreamy."

A heavy feeling was coming over me. I tried to keep it out of my voice as I asked, "And how did you get to watch me when the cabinet doesn't face that way?"

"Oh," she replied cautiously, "sometimes I can get the cabinet to swing open by itself."

"That's very clever," I said. "How exactly did you manage it?"

Alicia folded her arms under the back of her head and couldn't help but give a proud little smile. "I've learned a trick or two, you know. For example, look at your pillow."

I turned around and saw it beginning to hollow out in the middle, exactly at the place where her head was lying on it in the mirror.

"How did you do that?"

"I'm not sure. Willpower, I guess." Alicia smiled. "I'm getting stronger all the time, you know."

"Stronger?" I croaked. "Why? So you can spy on me?"

There was a silence. "No," she replied slowly. "So I can be useful to you."

"Like when you replaced me in the auditorium?" By now I was almost trembling with anger.

Alicia shrugged. "That worked out well for you, didn't it?"

"If you're thinking of doing the same thing tomorrow night, forget it."

Alicia sat up in the reflection of my bed. "That's ridiculous. I wouldn't risk having you turn against me by offering to go on a date in your place. I realize that I made a mistake by changing places with you without warning today, but—"

"That was so frightening!" I shouted at her. "What were those floating things grabbing at me in the blackness?"

"What blackness, Alice?"

"When I was in between mirrors."

"Oh, I wouldn't worry about *them*. They're hardly even things, Alice. They're the *Unformed*. Real losers who float around forever, hoping for just one chance to catch a look at real life from mirrors. I was one of them once, but I had the determination to break free! There were hundreds of the Unformed, maybe even thousands, who started fighting the moment you were born to be your one-and-only reflection, but I fought them off and beat them all out. Only once I got onto mirrors, I didn't stop there. I started to learn. That's the key to everything, Alice—knowledge and the drive to make it. Just look at me now. I have ideas, plans, projects you wouldn't believe—not even in your dreams."

Alicia's eyes suddenly blazed with a new light. "Speaking of dreams, Alice, wouldn't it be cool if I could find a way to start floating inside of yours? I could be there when you're sleeping, interacting in your imagination. You know, like some unseen computer program in cyberspace! Wouldn't it be neat?"

"No! And don't you dare! My mind is my own, do you understand me? My dreams are mine. My brain is mine! I don't even want to see you anymore on my mirrors!"

Alicia's face grew dark and threatening. She glared at me. "Alice, I am *not* going to give up my place as your reflection to some idiot from the Unformed. Not now, not ever. And if I were you, I wouldn't mention it again."

"All . . . all right," I said quickly. I was suddenly very scared.

"This is really awful," she said. "You should be grateful to me because of what I did for you in that auditorium. I did all that for *you*, Alice! Now you're making it seem as if I'm some sort of a monster." Her lips were pulled back over her gums. There was nothing beautiful about her now, not while she was snarling at me.

"I didn't mean it that way," I said softly. "Let's just drop this, okay?"

"Fine" she said, though she was still breathing heavily.

"Well, if everything's settled, I'm going to bed," I said. "See you tomorrow."

"Sleep tight," she said as I walked to my room, quietly but firmly shutting the bathroom door behind me.

But there was no rest for me. Maybe it was the eerie feeling that I was still being watched. I tried to relax by turning on the television and surfing the channels for something interesting. But that glowing screen—could Alicia be staring at me from it? As I shut it off, I caught a glint of moonlight on my wristwatch. Quickly I stripped it off, shoving it deep inside my pillowcase. Then I got up to roll the window shade all the way down.

But that left the room so dark that I couldn't help shuddering. It reminded me of that other blackness and those "Unformed" things! How could I go on like this?

All of a sudden, a strange noise prickled the hairs on my neck. What I heard was the faint sound of breathing. I caught my breath, to see if it was my own. No!

"Where are you, Alicia?" I asked softly.

"Perhaps I'm in your mind now," came the even softer reply, from where I could not tell.

"That's *crazy!*"

"Yes! Perhaps you *are* crazy, Alice. Maybe all of this has been happening in that head of yours."

"No, no, no!"

"Alice, even your wonderful friend Wendy thinks that's what it is. Only she doesn't dare tell you to your face what that really means—that you've gone insane."

"I'm not insane! I can't be!"

"Your mind is split in half, Alice. Give yourself over to me."

"No, I won't."

"Yes, then everything will be restful again."

"Alicia, go away. Get out of my head. Get off my mirrors. Get out of my life!"

"You can't make me, Alice. Do you know why? It's because you wanted me to be there for you! You wanted me to be bold where you were a wimp. To be charming and beautiful and clever where you weren't anything. What you wanted, Alice—what you *really* wanted—was for *you* to become *my* reflection!"

"That's a lie," I cried, but my head was throbbing, my chest pounding, my body quaking. Suddenly, a charge of electricity jolted me as straight as a board. I felt burning everywhere. My brain seemed to be on fire.

I fought back! My only thought was to rush to the bathroom and smash that mirror to pieces. The idea of doing it gave me the strength to get to my feet, though they were tingling like I was being electrocuted. Somehow I stumbled to the dresser, grabbed a flowerpot, and reached for the knob to the bathroom door. But it vibrated in my hand. Or was my hand shaking so hard I couldn't get hold of it? It didn't matter. I threw my body against the door. It gave way and I tumbled inside, clutching the flowerpot with both hands to keep from dropping it. Lifting it over my head, I staggered to the sink.

I was just about to smash it into the mirror when I caught a flash of Alicia leaping from it straight at me. Another jolt sent a flash of white fire blazing in my brain. It was the last thing I remembered before I heard a moaning cry.

At first I thought it was coming from me, but then I felt one of those sticky things touch the side of my face. It seemed to be trying to get ahead of me, to race past me.

"Stay back! Don't get in front of me," another Unformed thing hissed furiously. "It is my turn to replace Alicia on mirrors!"

I clawed at those sticky fingers and fought them off as I swam toward what looked like the edge of something shiny.

Other sticky things tugged at me, trying to pull me

back. I shrieked at them. I cursed. I kicked my feet and flailed in the darkness. I pushed my arms forward, groping, groping.

My hands moved slowly into light, then my head, my shoulders! I used all the strength of my mind, all my will—and suddenly, I was able to see my own bathroom.

See it, yes—but only from the mirror on the medicine cabinet! I had become a helpless reflection of Alicia. *She* was the one, not I, who stood solidly on the hard tiles of that floor.

And oh, how pleased with herself she was! I was still trying to grasp what had happened when her gloating began. "Say, Alice," she said, laughing, "wasn't it awfully clever of me to throw my voice before? Well, I won't have to play any tricks like that anymore. Because I am the person now. And I'll be a lot better at it than you ever were!"

I didn't try to reply. What could I say? That all along I'd been a fool to have anything to do with her? I felt so helpless, so empty inside. Maybe I didn't deserve to be anything but the mindless imitation of someone else!

My not responding seemed to annoy Alicia, and then to worry her. "Now listen," she warned, "if you can make any movement that isn't one of mine, Alice, or any sound of your own, you'd better show me now. That's how I'll know it's you on the glass reflecting me, not one of *them* who beat you to it. Believe me, you don't want me to decide that you're not worth bothering with anymore."

She seemed ready to make good on her threat and turn away. In another second I'd be floating in that void again. I tried to move my arms, but it seemed impossible. I gave orders for my mouth to open, but with hers closed that was impossible too. Did my eyes show my terror? I doubted it. No, I was convinced they were staring at her with exactly the same expression that she was directing at me. Maybe I didn't even have my zits. How I wanted my pimples now, just to show that *something* was left of me!

Alicia's impatience seemed to be giving her an itch and she scratched her nose. I had to do the same— only I felt nothing, not my skin, not even the itch! Inside myself I was screaming.

Suddenly my mouth moved. The words flew out. "This sucks!"

Alicia's smile returned. "Well, congratulations. Nice to have the same old Alice back. There has to be *somebody* around who can appreciate how much I've accomplished just by getting here. You must have put up quite a fight yourself not to have those Unformed things gang up and pull what was left of you apart so one of them could beat you out of your place as a mirror image. Remember, I was one of them myself. Now you know a tiny bit of what I had to go through to break out of that darkness. Maybe now you can appreciate what it was like for me to watch you and study you and wait for fifteen years for my chance to take your place here—in real life!"

Her smile had long since faded into the hardest look I had ever seen. How was I ever going to defeat someone like this? What chance did I have against an Unformed thing who had clawed her way into becoming another *me*?

But I had to. And I would.

"I know what you're thinking," Alicia said. "And you don't stand a chance against someone like me." She wagged a warning finger in my face. "It took me a long time to learn all the tricks of the void, Alice. And I still have connections among the Unformed. I can think of a dozen ways to pull in a replacement and get you off mirrors forever. Think about that. I'll see you later."

"Please don't leave yet!" I blurted.

"Sorry," she said lightly, "but now I'd like to try out the bed for real. I want to touch it and feel it under me and find out if it's really as cozy and warm as I'd always imagined."

"Just don't close the door," I pleaded as she started walking out.

"Oh, but I'm going to, Alice. Yes, indeed. After all, isn't that what you did when you wanted to shut *me* out? But before I do, let me hear you say that you're sorry that you ever tried to make problems for me."

"I'm sorry, Alicia."

"Say it louder, and mean it!"

"I'm sorry! I'm sorry!"

"Oh, that's a good little slave. Now what you should bear in mind for the rest of your days—no, the rest of *my* days—is how grateful you ought to be that you're somebody's reflection . . . especially somebody who might talk to you from time to time, if you make it worth her while. I want you to root for me to have a very long and very happy life. What's more, I think you'd better. I'm all you've got. Nighty-night."

I heard the door shut just before I plunged back into nothingness. Desperately, I tried to remember where those shiny places in the bedroom were that she had used to spy on me. But it was hard to think while terror rushed back over me.

Wait a minute. There was the plastic covering of my wristwatch! Oh, but that was still tucked inside the pillowcase. The television then. Was it on? And if so, how could I get to it? Would thinking about it help get me there? Or was I such a slave to Alicia that only her summons could draw me out of nothingness? Yet it seemed to me that if Alicia had been able to manage a few tricks, why couldn't I? I tried very hard to concentrate. And for just a single moment, I found myself flashing into the blinding light on the surface of a lightbulb. But then it was gone. Or I was gone.

Now the darkness closed completely around me. I felt unseen presences buzzing past me. The air was filled with their whispers.

Then they were gone! It seemed as if some change of attitude toward me had just taken place among the Unformed. Apparently anyone who had become established as the image of a living person was given plenty of room. I was glad that the horror of having to fight them off had passed. Yet at the same time, I felt even more alone than before. I drifted in a deep, completely black space.

No light. Nothing to touch . . . or to breathe . . . or even to hear. Was this the same as being dead? Maybe not, because I could still think. Yet perhaps that made it even worse, since all my mind could tell me was that I was alone in a vast nowhere . . . and that I myself was *nothing*.

Chapter 8

After what felt like forever, I was suddenly yanked out of the darkness to reflect Alicia going down the stairs in daylight.

It seemed to me that I was mirroring her from below, maybe from the glass door of the china cabinet. I could hear my mother in the kitchen, playing her old Beatles tape turned way down so as not to annoy my father. But Alicia went by so quickly that in a flash I was back in nothingness, wanting desperately to see my home—and my parents—again!

I got my wish, sort of, when I found myself up very close to Alicia's mouth but moving back from it. A second later I was far enough away to see all of her face, though there was something in the middle blocking my view. What was I reflecting her from?

Of course! I was on a tablespoon while she was eating breakfast. The smudge was a small bit of oatmeal that hadn't come off in her mouth! How ridiculously proud of myself I was for figuring that out.

Looking back on it now, it was so pathetic of me to make such a big thing out of nothing. But what else could I do when everything connected to real life was slipping so far away from me? I simply had to cling to whatever I could keep my mind on.

The next thing I knew, I had turned up on the long hallway mirror. While Alicia was opening the coat closet, I saw my chance to reason with her. "Do you really mean to keep me like this forever and ever?" I asked.

"Don't be such a drag," she said.

"What was that, dear?" my mother called.

"It's this droopy coat of mine, Mom. This thing is for kids in sandboxes."

"What are you *talking* about?" my mother demanded in exasperation. "You only got it for your last birthday, and you loved it!"

"Well, I hate it now. I'm not going to wear it."

"But you'll freeze!"

"I'd rather freeze than help lead a strike looking like a two-year-old."

My mother stormed into the living room. "Alice, your father is going to file for bankruptcy if we go shopping for a new coat after everything else that we bought."

"It's not a problem, Mom. I'm going. 'Bye!"

"Wait a minute. Take my heavy one!"

"What? The thing with the fur collar? People will think I'm in favor of killing animals!"

"Alice, you *eat* animals!"

"Well, I don't have to make a display of it! You don't wear that coat yourself anymore."

"All right, take my new blue one from Lands' End. But treat it carefully. It's hardly even out of the box."

"Oh, that's so *nice* of you, Mom! You're a blessing!"

Alicia threw me a wink as she darted for the door. "See how easy it all is when you know what you're doing?" she whispered.

"Easy to be selfish!" I flung at her, before she blacked me out again.

All my thoughts were on finding places to reflect her from. I had to find out if I had any control over that. In the midst of the nothingness that surrounded me, I concentrated on seeing her. Finally I caught a flash of her on the street outside our house. Judging from the sound of heavy rumbling behind me, I guessed I was on the side mirror of a passing truck. But when a parked car blocked my chance to keep on reflecting Alicia, I fell into the blackness again. Still, I tried to hope that just maybe I was gaining some power over my bizarre existence.

I returned to the world for a much longer time after Alicia got on the school bus. I popped up on the rearview mirror and on one or two of the windows. Alicia had the coat over her arm by then, even though it must have been cold in there, and I couldn't believe how much she was swinging her hips walking down the aisle. This was also a surprise to the white-haired woman who was driving the bus. I could tell that she didn't like it at all. But all the boys certainly did, even if a few of the girls grew wide-eyed.

"Just my rendition of the Student Body!" Alicia called out cheerily, and everyone broke up. Then she dropped into Davy DeWitt's row, though he wasn't on the bus. It was almost as if she was making a claim for everyone to see that this was where she belonged.

The real Student Body was standing beside Davy in front of the school when the bus pulled up. She was part of the organizing crowd, some of whom were handing out clean rags to those who hadn't brought any gags to put in their mouths. Trust her to be right in front of the two reporters, posing for shots in her sexy version of a striped prison outfit and giving interviews! Others were distributing computer printouts that gave advice on how to behave in the classrooms all day. It boiled down to being very, very polite and very, very silent.

Alicia simply smiled at David, who looked a little sheepish having the Student Body's hand on his arm. She paused before going inside to sign a petition for the reinstatement of the Social Studies teacher, the school production, and free speech in general. On her way to homeroom, she ducked into the girls' room to check on her appearance. Apparently I wasn't making that easy for her.

"You're not reflecting me right with that ugly scowl on your face," she snapped, after checking out the stalls to make sure no one could hear her speaking to herself.

"I guess you think I ought to be happy?"

"I think you ought to be smart. You don't want to make me mad, Alice, believe me."

"Oh?" I sneered back. "What more can you do to me?"

"I can stop looking at you, and I can certainly stop talking to you! Do you want that?"

"No," I admitted, disheartened.

"Okay, then. How do I look?"

"All right."

Her eyebrows lifted. "That's all? Not sensational?"

"You . . . you look very good."

"Hey, don't overwhelm me with all these compliments," Alicia said archly. Then she paused and began again. "Look, Alice, at first I was glad that it was you who turned up as my image and not one of the Unformed. Now I'm beginning to think it's a mistake for both of us if you're going to torture yourself instead of accepting the situation. So maybe you ought to step aside for one of them. Let yourself drift and stop thinking. Forget who you ever were. Yes, that might be best, after all."

"Thanks for the wonderful advice," I told her coldly.

She gave me a long look, stuffed a gag in her mouth, and was gone.

I picked her up again in homeroom. Even in the midst of my own horror, I still cared how the rest of the school day went for Alicia and everyone else. It was my connection to life, so I did everything I could to find places from which to reflect her so I could see what was going on.

For Alicia, the day was a triumph. That good-humored, devil-may-care look in her eyes lit up everyone around her. It was an inspiration to other students, who, after the novelty of being gagged wore off, were in danger of getting bored out of their minds.

But Alicia lost her cool in Signing class when Wendy tried to make hand conversation. Alicia wouldn't return Wendy's usual I-love-you gesture, instead shooting her the coldest drop-dead look. That made me so furious, I decided to say something about it the next time I had the chance.

I thought an opportunity to talk might turn up during lunch period, but I was sadly mistaken. Alicia didn't go into the girls' room, maybe because it was crowded. And the cafeteria, where the gags had to come off so people could eat, was in an uproar, with everyone talking or shouting at once. I saw all this first while shining off one part of the cash register as Alicia paid for her lunch, then from another part as she went by with her tray on the way to a table. But when somebody else's body passed between us, I landed on the casing of the big wall clock that overlooked the room.

That move gave me a little bit of a thrill for two reasons. First, I had hopped over to the clock without going through any blackness at all. Second, I had thought of that jump *before* it happened. I was almost sure that I had caused activity in the real world!

I saw Alicia weaving toward a table near the back where David DeWitt was standing up, waving her over. I watched her by glancing over my shoulder while she and I were both moving away from each other. It gave me the strangest feeling because, since she was doing the same thing, it seemed to me that she was looking straight at me, too—and gloating.

Once Alicia sat down, she and Davy started to talk. I couldn't hear anything from that far away, of course, especially with so much noise. The room got quiet pretty quickly, though, after the loudspeaker crackled. The announcement instructed all students and faculty to come immediately to an assembly in the auditorium to hear the superintendent of schools.

The Student Council members gathered in a huddle. Alicia and the Student Body went more or less face-to-face when they were called over. I got into it also, suddenly finding myself—and what a wild jump this was!—reflecting Alicia from the twin irises of the Student Body's green eyes.

Everyone but the Student Body agreed with Alicia

that all the students should be asked to put their gags back in their mouths, file quietly into the auditorium, and sit there, saying nothing. For her part, the Student Body declared that if she didn't like what the superintendent had to say, she was going to tie her gag into a ball and throw it at the woman and get everyone else to do the same.

The others got upset, and David DeWitt told her that showing off like that would ruin the reasonable purpose of the strike. But Alicia gave her a challenging little smile that seemed to say, "Why don't you just do it, honey, and make a *complete* fool of yourself?"

Whether the Student Body would have gone through with her threat or not no one ever got to find out. The superintendent of schools wasn't anything like the principal. While he sat rigidly on the stage with the corners of his mouth twitching, she strode up to the mike looking very relaxed and even a little amused by several hundred upturned faces with gags stuffed between their teeth.

She began by saying that our strike reminded her of the days when she demonstrated against the Vietnam War and joined marches for civil rights. She said she was glad to see that students today were also idealistic and cared about basic liberties.

Yet at the same time she wanted to ask us all to "walk in the shoes" of a dedicated school principal who has a job to do and a basic right to act according to his own point of view on how best to perform that job. She said it was to his credit that he had made an effort to walk in the shoes of his students. In fact, it was he who had called her the night before to see what could be done to resolve the conflict.

The two of them had discussed the situation for a long time and had come up with some ideas. Number one: Through the elected Student Council, the students would be asked to propose their own reasonable—and she wanted to stress the word *reasonable*—code of dress. Number two: The students would not all be punished for the actions of some, and there was nothing to prevent the drama club from immediately resuming production of the play.

At this point, there was a storm of happy feet banging. It came to a halt, though, when David DeWitt stood up to swing his arms in an everybody-hold-off gesture.

After a glance at the principal, the superintendent drew a deep breath and brought up what she said was "the so-called issue" of the Social Studies teacher being fired. In reality, this was *not* an issue, she explained, since it "had arisen out of the very faulty mathematical practice of adding two and two together and getting twenty-two."

There was a lot of shifting around in the auditorium and grunting through the gags, which made her call out, "Am I losing my credibility already?"

When this brought hundreds of nods, she shook her head and said, "Well, let me go on." Then she admitted that yes, there had been a "heated discussion" between the principal and Mr. Simms over what he had said in the teachers' lounge. Regardless of the rights and wrongs of that discussion, however, nobody had been fired. The teacher had simply complained of a migraine and taken the rest of the day off. It was only after he got home that he discovered he had come down with a bad case of flu, which was why he stayed out a few days more. This was all that had happened. The rest was the result of jumping to conclusions without stopping to check the facts.

"Well, that's it," she said. "You decide whether you want to continue your strike or not."

The superintendent started walking away, but before she could leave the stage, Alicia jumped up from her seat in the front row to lead the applause. The gags came out, and everyone cheered.

Once people started to leave, Alicia got so mixed into the crowd that I went spinning off into nothingness again. In the halls I made some split-second contact, briefly glinting here and there off someone's eyeglasses while Alicia milled around, laughing and being popular.

All this made me dizzy. When Alicia finally got to my afternoon classes, where either the windows or the wall clocks reflected me, it was party time there, too. None of the students could stay seated long enough to do any work, and the teachers gave up trying to make them.

At one point, Alicia actually opened the compact on her lap. Was it just so I could see how radiant she was? So she could gloat in my face over how much fun she was having hijacking my life? It was so disgusting, I actually closed my eyes, until I heard her whispering, "How can I be friendly and share anything with someone who's being so stupid?" She snapped the compact closed.

As I sailed out into nothingness, I repeated to myself what she'd said. It made me wonder if I hadn't just made a big mistake, if I wasn't missing an opportunity. What did I have to lose by appealing to her to show fairness? How could I know for sure that she'd turn me down if I asked for us to trade places on a regular basis?

I got my chance after school when Alicia went into the house and stopped by the hallway closet to hang up Mom's coat. "Alicia, I'm sorry that I turned away from you before," I said quietly from the mirror.

"It's about time," Alicia replied with a resentful toss of her head, "that you learned to keep your place."

"You're right. I will."

"Good," she said, and started to walk away.

I spoke quickly to stop her. "Look, I know you're not completely happy about putting me in this spot. You're too decent for that. I also know that I had a lot to do with your coming more alive on mirrors the way you did. Maybe all the energy I fed into you made it more awful for you to be stuck on mirrors."

"Is there a point to this?" said Alicia.

"Yes . . . uh . . ." She was giving me such a peculiar stare that I started to stammer. "What I'm trying to suggest . . . is . . . uh . . . a kind of sharing that—"

Alicia's hand went up to cut me off. "*Sharing?*" she snorted. "You can talk to me about *sharing* when you've spent fifteen years on glass like I have."

"Oh, God! I have to wait until then to even discuss it?"

"No. I can give you my answer right now. Here, let me put it this way."

Then the me with the perfect face spat a thick glob onto my image and walked away.

Chapter 9

"I shouldn't have spat at you, Alice. I'm sorry."

Incredibly, that apology came from Alicia's own lips after dinner. She said it to me after opening the compact once more—this time on the desk in my bedroom. Did that mean she was actually ready to start talking about a compromise? Not at all. It was an hour or so before *my* date with David DeWitt, and she had spread out her homework assignment in front of my face.

"Do me a favor," she went on, "and show me how to get this stuff done. Dad is sweet, but—"

"Don't call him Dad! He's not your father!"

"Oh, but he is now," she said with a smile. "And as I was saying, he's sweet, but he can also be a problem. He's laid down the law that, since there's school tomorrow, all this homework has to be done before I can go out. And, well, this isn't the kind of thing that I ever paid any attention to when I was hopping about on mirrors. So how about it?"

"Not a chance!"

"Oh, really," she replied coolly. Her eyes narrowed. "Maybe you should look at it this way. Just because I'm in this world now, that doesn't mean I've given up my contacts with the Unformed. So far they are leaving you alone while you serve me. But as soon as I send word that it's all right with me if one of them takes your place, they will all pounce on you when you're between mirrors and tear what's left of you to shreds. Then you'll float in bits and pieces forever with no chance of ever seeing light again! Now, are you going to help me whenever I ask for it?"

I was too shaken to do anything but nod.

"Oh, Alice, that's so lovely of you!" she exclaimed, breaking into one of her most charming smiles. "You're being so good to me!"

"Yeah . . . right," I mumbled, reading the triumph in her eyes as she gloated over my weakness.

So there I was, poring over homework while all Alicia had to do was write out what I told her. Finally it was time for my mother to drive Alicia to her date. I got to go along on the rearview mirror on the passenger side.

We were entering the downtown section when my mother began to preach. "It's not that I don't trust your good judgment, dear. But . . . uh . . . I know how you like this boy. Promise me you won't let him do anything you're not ready for."

"Mom!"

"All right, all right! But you're only fifteen, you know."

"Would you mind holding on to the wheel with both hands?" Alicia asked.

"I'm holding it. You're making me nervous. Now that you've changed the way you dress and everything else, that's all the more reason to take some care and to value yourself."

Alicia leaned across to kiss my mom's cheek. "That's very good advice. You don't have to worry about me, really."

My mother gave a little sigh. "So what time shall I pick you up?"

"Midnight."

"Are you *insane?* You've got school tomorrow!"

"So I'll be a little sleepy."

"Forget it. I'm coming at ten. And don't you be stubborn with me when I get there."

"Eleven."

"Ten! And that's it!"

"Mom!" Alicia thumped back in her seat. "If you're going to be that unreasonable about the first and only date I've ever had in my life, then why am I even going? I won't have a chance to talk to Davy when he's playing. And then there'll be other people around wanting to—"

"Enough! Eleven."

Alicia laughed. "You're such a sweetie, Mom. There's no one like you."

There was no one like Alicia, either. Right from

the very start she could manage my mother much better than I ever did . . . or thought was right.

My mother had gone by the time I found another place to reflect from. I didn't know what I'd landed on until I realized from a bunch of black knobs poking out around me that I was on the gleaming metal surface of an espresso machine. Alicia was already sitting down with her elbow propped on a table. She was holding a cigarette between her fingers—straight up like one of those nightclub singers in old black-and-white movies who had throaty voices and heavy-lidded eyes and wore glittering evening gowns. Boy, it was so phony!

David didn't seem to mind when he came down from the stand where he was testing out the sound equipment. He swung into the seat next to her, and they got very close real soon.

Meanwhile, the crowd was pouring in—mostly teens, but one guy seemed to be in his twenties. He came over to shake hands with David and to be introduced to Alicia. He sat down on the other side of her, and the three of them did a lot of kidding around. Then I saw the older guy lean over to whisper something in her ear.

I didn't like *that* at all, especially when Alicia secretly lowered her coffee cup below the table so he could pour something into it. For all of Alicia's grown-up ways, there was something very naive about her. If only she had opened her compact, I could have warned her to be careful drinking that stuff.

Pretty soon David's band got up to play. When people started to dance, the moving bodies cut me off from Alicia until she began dancing, too. Even then, I kept being blocked out whenever others got between us. I felt like a light switch clicking on and off, on and off. Of course, every time I vanished, so did the sound, and every time I came back, I got a deafening blast. Soon I was so dizzy that I had no idea whether minutes or hours were passing.

The next thing I knew, Alicia was in a phone booth. She closed the door to turn on the inside light and opened the compact, knowing that I'd be on it. She wanted to get my home phone number from me.

"Alicia, I wonder if you knew what you were doing before when you let that guy—"

"Not now," she said, dialing. "I'm too excited about the news."

"What news?"

"Just wait a minute and you'll hear." The phone was ringing, and then it was picked up. "Mom! You'll never guess!"

Alicia held the receiver so I could hear my mother's voice too. "David's told you he likes you."

"Yes, but that's not it! He's going to nominate me to be Homecoming Queen!"

"Excuse me?"

"Mom, you never heard of Homecoming Queen?"

My mother sounded puzzled. "Do they still have such things?"

"Of course they do! The celebration takes place the last weekend of the football season, for the final home game."

"Well, that sounds like quite an honor. Tell me, how does it work? I mean, what do you get from being Homecoming Queen if—"

"Get from it? If I'm elected, that means I'm the most beautiful girl in the school."

"Well, it's wonderful that David feels that way about you, dear. And you certainly do look lovely. But isn't this the kind of thing one of the cheerleaders usually wins?"

"Yes. And there's one of them everybody calls the Student Body who thinks she's got it locked up. But it's also like politics, Mom, and she's made a lot of other girls feel down about her. Also, Davy's the president of the Student Council. So if *he* proposes me, I think—"

"Well, it certainly is exciting, dear."

Alicia's smile froze. "Then why don't you sound excited?"

"I am! I don't want you to start feeling that it's a matter of life and death, that's all. You know, just in case—"

"Mom, I'm telling you, I'm going to make it work out! I want you to be happy for me!"

"Darling, you misunderstand me if you think I'm not." My mother was growing flustered. "We'll talk about it more when I come to pick you up."

But a hard tone came into Alicia's voice as she said, "You needn't bother. The manager of David's band has a car, and he's driving me home."

"That's out of the question, Alice. I don't know him."

"But David knows him. And I've asked you to call me Alicia. See you later, Mom."

"Wait a minute. I—"

Alicia hung up and glanced down at me. "What is it, Alice? What do *you* want?"

I was so angry I could barely speak. But she knew exactly what I was thinking, so she said straight out, "Don't bother arguing, Alice. This is my life now. I'm not sharing it with you, and I'm not going to take your advice on how to behave."

"But you can't treat my mother like that!"

"I can do anything I want. That's how it's going to be," Alicia replied firmly.

"We'll see about that!" I shrieked, but she snapped the compact shut and plunged me into darkness again.

I won't dwell on what happened in that guy's car. At first I shut my eyes and tried to block up my ears.

When I heard a tap-tapping on the mirror, though, I couldn't help looking at Alicia and caught her mischievous grin. I realized she was showing off for me.

"Alicia, cut that out," I yelled when I couldn't take it anymore. "He thinks you're me! And I wouldn't do anything like that!"

"That's just what I thought," she said mockingly. "Keep on watching and you'll learn something."

"Hold it a minute," said the guy. "I didn't get that. What's up? What did you say?"

"Oh, I'm just having a conversation in my mind with someone who doesn't want me to be doing what I'm doing. But I *am* doing it, aren't I?"

"You sure are, baby," he said enthusiastically. "Just like a big girl."

"I *am* a big girl!"

I tried to feel that it didn't matter what people would think of her. But it did—because of my parents and, even more important, because of myself. Somehow, some way, though I didn't yet know how, I was going to get my life back!

Chapter 10

Alicia was so smooth the way she went about conducting her campaign for Homecoming Queen. She would walk over to the other girls when they were hanging around in groups at the lockers or outside study hall. Then she'd stand there quietly until she got the hang of the conversation. Finally she'd join in, not saying anything at all about the vote, just letting them see what a nice person she was. If any of them said something catty about the Student Body, she would reply that everybody has faults. Then she'd think of some very sincere-sounding compliment to give one of the girls before she left.

She never stopped to talk with the boys, because that could tick off their girlfriends. She'd just sail on past them in the halls, while trying to catch what they were talking about, then make a funny comment that left them stunned and impressed.

The one person she stayed as far away from as possible was Wendy. Alicia kept ducking her at school, and whenever Wendy called her at home, she'd brush her off with a bunch of excuses. Finally, though, she couldn't avoid talking with her. It happened one evening at the movies, and it was really horrible.

I was reflecting from the huge mirror that ran across the wall behind the candy counter. David and Alicia were waiting in front of it for one of the six cinemas to empty out so they could go in for the second show. Wendy had just gotten her ticket and was coming in. She saw them and stopped a ways off, looking as if she wanted to come over.

Before she could decide, the earlier crowd came out. Who should be among them but the Student Body! As soon as David spotted her, he looked as if he'd been caught in church stealing from the poor box.

"Now isn't this interesting, Davy," she said, walking up to him. "You told me that you had to rehearse with your band tonight. But here you are with her!"

"Yeah, well—" David began, then broke off in confusion.

Alicia smiled and said, "So how was the movie? Will Davy and I like it, do you think?" She tucked her hand under his arm very possessively.

The Student Body turned to David, seething. "She's been coming on with other guys behind your back, Davy. Two from the basketball team that I know of, because the cheerleaders they've been seeing told me. And that big guy who plays tackle on your squad. He told me so himself. He said she'd do almost anything to get votes. Pretty soon, Davy boy, you'll have to stand in line and buy tickets for *her!*"

All this was going on quite loudly, and a lot of people were watching. I waited to see what Alicia would do.

"Well, this is all a total lie, of course," Alicia said calmly. "Naturally she can get her cheerleader friends to back her up in anything. But it's really such a low way to get back at me for daring to be in the same contest that she is. All I said to that fellow on your team was that he played very gracefully. That's how he looked to me when I saw you all at practice. The only reason I complimented him was that he looked so depressed after the coach called him a big dumb ox! Was it so terrible, Davy, that I tried to make him feel better about himself?"

David said no, and the Student Body got so fed up that she marched off. But I could see that he was still shaken up. A moment later, he started heading for the exit.

"Where are you going?" Alicia called after him.

"I'll be right back."

"You're not going to *apologize* to her, are you?"

"No! I . . . uh . . . just have to clear my head," he called back and left the theater quickly.

It was then that Wendy came over, looking very determined and brave. "This isn't easy for me, Alice," she began. "But every time I try calling you to see what you're doing about that talking character in the mirrors, you hurry me off the phone."

"No, I don't hurry you off," Alicia insisted roughly. "I've told you several times that, yes, you were right and that I'm aware it was a fantasy. I've gotten over it. What *more* do you want?"

"But you're calling yourself Alicia now."

"So what? I like that name."

"Why do you keep avoiding me in school?"

"I don't avoid you," Alicia snapped at her. "If I'm going to win that vote for Homecoming Queen, I've got lots to do. As you can see from what happened to me just now, some people would do and say anything to stop me. And how, may I ask, are *you* helping? Is there any reason why I have to be doing all of this by myself? It would be a lot nicer if somebody else also campaigned for me. If you're really my friend, you'll do that instead of being so jealous."

Wendy's mouth fell open. "But I'm not jealous."

"Oh, why can't you be *honest?*" Alicia stormed. "Then maybe we could mend what's wrong with our friendship! You don't like to see me looking so much better than I ever did before. Can't you own up to it?"

"But you're wrong. I do like it."

"That's such bull! People tell so many lies around here! You just want to drag me all the way back to how Alice was before I ever came along! What you want is for me not to be any better than *you*—a real loser!"

Wendy swallowed hard, and I could see she was fighting back tears. Then a strange light came over her that almost gave me hope. "You said 'drag me back to how Alice was before I came along.' You talk as if Alice is somebody else you've taken over."

Wendy was actually staring at the mirror now, looking straight past Alicia's left shoulder at the real me! Desperately I tried to move my head to a different position from Alicia's, to open my lips and say something directly to Wendy, even to lift my hands and make distress signs!

But nothing worked. Nothing! I had no control over my image.

When Wendy turned her gaze back to Alicia, I threw all the will I had into the wildest, most frantic attempt of all. I tried to communicate with Wendy's own mirror image.

It was useless. That image was simply an Unformed thing that had made it as far as becoming a reflection of her but nothing more.

And then, from out of the shadows of nothingness, floated an old man's voice. "You'll get nothing out of that one, child. Only a very few of us can ever communicate with each other."

Now I saw the other image. It was the reflection of an elegantly dressed man with a hard, cruel face who was crossing in front of the candy counter.

"Who are you?" I asked in amazement, using thought rather than spoken words.

"Oh, no one in particular now, but forty years ago I was mayor of this city. Actually *he* became mayor. He offered me help when I was having a breakdown over the death of my wife. There was going to be an election debate with my rival, don't you see, but I just wasn't up to it. I didn't have the heart to trade arguments and insults with anyone then. So I let him take over after he promised to change places with me again. But they rarely do, even much later in life when they fall into the worst of health. See how his hand is shaking! No," moaned the reflection with terrible sadness, "I shall never even die in my own bed. Well, I must go now. Good luck to you, child. You'll need it."

I watched him go. Wendy had left without my noticing, and David had returned to the cinema. He looked glum but still ready to take Alicia into the show.

That man's words filled my mind. Forty years he had spent like this. How long would it be for me if I couldn't find a way to push Alicia out and take back my life?

Alicia was gazing at me now as she headed for the show. Just a passing glance, yet the icy look in her eyes sent a shiver of terror through me.

Chapter 11

No sooner had I vanished into nothingness again than a cloud of the Unformed swarmed, attacking me through the blackness. Maybe Alicia had overheard my conversation with the old man and decided to punish me.

This time, I almost saw the fluttering shapes— darker than the darkness. They came at me with teeth like needles and gouging claws. Even though I had no body, I felt the rips, the bites, the screaming pain!

I lashed out at them, but they had no bodies to grab hold of or push away. I passed through them as if they were ghosts! Suddenly I realized that since I had no body either, all this was happening in my mind. Alicia was driving me insane!

Later that night, after she got home from the movie, I heard her laughter. She was on the phone talking to Davy. No, to that guy who'd taken her home from Espresso the night she'd been drinking. She wanted me to hear the garbage they were saying to each other. She wanted me to hear what a fun, sexy time she was having with *my* life!

Meanwhile, those batlike things were clawing at

me. I knew why she had sent them: to make me let go of what was left of myself, to give up my mind and abandon my spirit, to forget the knowledge that I was still *me!* Finally I realized that Alicia had never intended to help me. Our so-called deal was a trick. She wanted me to become an empty form in the nothingness!

Her plan backfired, because the idea of losing my spirit was so awful that it helped me fight back. It pulled me out of my terror and calmed me. Immediately, the angry stings of the Unformed began to lessen, and their batlike wings stopped flapping around me. I was alone again in the blackness.

This time, however, I felt stronger. My fear had turned into a resolve to survive.

After several days of concentrated effort, I finally got the medicine-cabinet door in the bathroom to swing open. That way, I could sometimes see into the bedroom when Alicia was lying in bed, which she loved to do.

One day she was lying on her stomach on top of the covers, turning the pages of some raggy gossip magazine. Suddenly my mom yelled at Alicia to come downstairs. When Alicia called back that she was busy, my dad came up to get her.

"Why, what's so important?" she demanded.

"Wendy Bauer is downstairs saying things about

you that are really distressing to your mother and me."

"*What?*" Alicia bounded to her feet. "How could you let her come here?"

"She rang the bell. What were we supposed to do?"

"But she's talking about me without my being there!"

"That's exactly why we stopped her, Alice."

"*Alice,*" she snarled, "is not my—"

My father was giving her a wide-eyed stare, and she suddenly caught herself. "Sorry, Dad," she said. "Alice is fine. Alicia just sounds so much nicer to me, that's all." She kissed him on the cheek. "It's my way of getting over how mousy I used to feel."

"Well, that sounds reasonable," he conceded.

"I'll be right down."

As soon as he left the room, she made a big effort to get herself together. Then she took a deep breath, paused for a moment or two, and went out.

It seemed to me that I actually jumped ahead of her onto the glass front of the china cabinet before she came down the stairs. Wendy was in the living room, talking to my agitated mother. Alicia walked in, looking just as relaxed as they were tense.

"Hi, Wendy," she said brightly. "Are you okay?"

"Not really, Alice. I know you don't want me talking to your parents about this, but I'm so worried about you that I just have to!"

Alicia lifted a hand. "That's all right. That's fine.

Actually, it's my fault that you needed to come here."

My mother looked as if she were grasping at straws. "How is it your fault, dear?"

"I've been neglecting Wendy. I'm sure that'll stop as soon as I get used to all these changes I've been going through."

My mother's voice quivered. "What changes do you mean, dear?"

"Oh, working on myself. Changing my attitude about my appearance. Getting more used to talking to people. Going out with a guy." Alicia directed a big smile at my father. "Even letting him kiss me, Dad. But don't be upset about that."

"I'm . . . er . . . I'm not upset," he mumbled.

"I've even been giving Mom a hard time by having my own ideas about what time to come home—though it was never very late, except that once. Was it, Mom?"

"No, not really. But, darling, Wendy has a feeling that you've . . ."

She paused, and Alicia turned to Wendy. "That I've what?"

"I've told them about your talking mirror image."

"Mom, I tried to tell you about that myself."

"Perhaps you did. But Wendy says it's still going on."

"Really? I don't see how she would know that since we've hardly spent any time together lately."

Wendy stood up. "That's because you're letting this thing take you over, and you don't want me to interfere. But, Alice, I have to! You need to go to therapy. And—"

Alicia gently interrupted her. "No, Wendy. I love you, but I have to say this straight out. You need to get yourself a life. I can't supply that. There are so many new things that have come into my life lately that I know it's a threat to you. I know it means that we have less to share. But if you could just make the effort to come along with me and be happy for me . . ."

"That does sound reasonable," my father declared.

"Mr. Shea, I'm telling you she's possessed!" Wendy nearly shouted.

"That's not the sort of thing my wife and I believe in."

"No, it isn't," my mother added. "Wendy, we're terribly sorry. We know you mean this for the best. And . . ."

As my mother faltered, Wendy instantly jumped in. "You're both misunderstanding me. I'm trying to save Alice from this idea that caught hold of her because she couldn't stand how she looked! I'm telling you she actually believes that the Alicia she saw on the mirror is better than she is and deserves to be the one who lives her life. So now she's let Alicia take her over completely, and Alice is somewhere inside underneath it! I am telling you this mirror image is strangling your child and my friend. Oh, won't you please listen to me and take her to a doctor!"

"I don't want to say anything that might hurt you," declared my mother. "But I do think—and I imagine my husband does also—that you've been feeling very much abandoned by Alice."

My father nodded, and she went on. "That it's hurt you a lot is understandable. You two have been inseparable for years."

"Half the time, I forgot that you weren't our own," put in my father with a sad little smile.

"But, dear, Alice has been developing in a new direction lately. Some of it concerns us a little, too, because at times she seems to be growing up a bit too fast. But much of it we think is wonderful. So it makes me terribly unhappy to suggest that perhaps I was wrong not to agree with *your* mother. Perhaps it *was* best for the two of you to, well . . ."

"But it has nothing to *do* with—" Wendy's hands covered her face. She burst into tears and ran for the door.

As soon as she left, my worried father began muttering to himself. That was more than my mother could take. "I do wish you would stop swallowing your words whenever there's something on your mind!"

"Well, I don't know if I should be talking about the medical condition of my customers," said my father, who owns a drugstore. "I'm thinking about Wendy's thyroid problem and the medication she takes for it. She's supposed to take one tablet in the morning, one at night. But I can't for the life of me recall when I last refilled her bottle. Perhaps all this is because she's been neglecting—"

"Well, she sure needs *something*," blurted Alicia. "That was so upsetting!"

"Now, now." As I watched in total disgust, my mother hurried over to hug and kiss her. "You were very nice to Wendy in spite of everything she said, and we're proud of you. Right, James?"

She waited for my dad to say so, too, but his thoughts were elsewhere. "I'm trying to remember whether it was like this for me."

"Like what, Dad?" asked Alicia, pretending there was a reason for wiping her eyes.

"Growing up. It can be so painful."

Now they were both making nicey-nice to Alicia. The sight of that on top of everything else made me want to get away. But since I couldn't actually leave on my own, I blanked out. My awareness didn't come back until Alicia began barking directly into my face.

By then I was up in my bathroom and Alicia was glaring at me as if I had caused the scene downstairs.

Gone was the sorrowful look and all those other winning expressions Alicia could put on and off so easily. "Is this you, Alice, or have you been replaced yet? I want an answer!"

"It's me," I said evenly, looking her straight in the eye.

"Good, because I want you to hear this. I realize clearly now that Wendy is my enemy. She won't stop. I can see that! She's going to try and get at me any way she can. She'll talk against me at school. She'll poison everybody's mind. She'll make them think I'm a nut! And who is going to vote for a wacko to be Homecoming Queen? Nobody! Alice, if I have to kill your precious friend to stop her, that's exactly what I'll do. I'll kill her!"

Chapter 12

I didn't doubt that Alicia was serious about murdering Wendy if she got in her way. What I completely failed to realize at first—stupid me!—was her obsession to find evidence that my friend was working against her at school.

As far as I could see, her campaign to beat out the Student Body for Homecoming Queen was working perfectly. It's true that the girls may not have been wildly *for* Alicia, but at least they thought she was less of a show-off than her only competition. As for the boys, maybe they didn't go totally crazy whenever she went by like they did over the Student Body. But with just a few words and some eye contact, Alicia could make almost any guy feel special.

So there she was, with everything getting better and better. Yet somehow Alicia couldn't shake the feeling that Wendy was secretly pulling strings behind her back that would make everything fall apart at the last minute.

As the day for the vote drew closer, this need to make sure she wasn't losing anyone's support had her rushing around so crazily that David DeWitt finally told her he just didn't feel she was there for him anymore. Alicia hadn't shown the slightest interest when she learned that his band was falling apart. Now David let Alicia know that if she had, he would have explained the problem. He told her that when the manager bragged about her having been ready to try anything the night he drove her home from Espresso, David had called him a liar and knocked him cold!

But there was even more on David's mind. He announced to Alicia that if she had wished him happy birthday, that might have been nice, but since her mind was obviously somewhere else, maybe it would be better if they just called it quits.

Listening to David's outburst, I was a little surprised that he was so focused on his birthday. Then I realized that that had been just the latest of many recent snubs from Alicia, and he was using it as a way of expressing his hurt.

It was clear that Alicia had no real interest in David or anyone else—only herself. She saw him as her property, to keep or get rid of when she chose. How dare he not keep on adoring her? Someday soon she'd make him pay for this, but right now she needed to patch things up. So her phony song and dance began.

Alicia agreed that David had good reason to be upset with her and apologized for being so caught up in what she called "this Homecoming Queen thing" that she had badly neglected him. Then she praised

David for not letting his manager get away with telling that horrible lie about her, just because she had turned him down flat when he made a pass, and promised him that soon they'd have all the time in the world together. Finally she told him how he had already brought her so much happiness that she could hardly explain, but she would understand if he now wanted to move on to somebody else.

Before David knew what was going on, Alicia had *him* trying to convince *her* that there couldn't be anybody but her! By the time they got to school, she had the poor guy eating out of her hand again like he was her puppy dog.

At that point I really lost sympathy for David, though why I put anybody else down for becoming Alicia's victim, I don't know. At any rate, Alicia thought she had won David over. But near the end of the day, she spotted David talking to Wendy—and she completely freaked!

Alicia didn't show her feelings to anybody else, but of course I got a load of them in private. Her hatred of Wendy skyrocketed. As soon as my father came home for supper that evening, she made an excuse to leave the house. It was one of the few times she took my bike.

A little while later, I reflected her from the window of my dad's drugstore and saw her put down the kickstand. After that I jumped from surface to surface inside the store. I wasn't going to let Alicia out of my sight!

A young druggist who worked for my dad was there by himself. He was a pretty nice person, a very gentle kind of guy. He was shy like me, and his face had marks on it like he'd never really gotten over his own skin problems.

He gave Alicia a friendly smile, saying he'd heard all about her running for Homecoming Queen and he wished her a lot of luck. Right away she began telling him a cooked-up story—how she was thinking of surprising her father by taking up chemistry in college and then going on to learn how to be a druggist. She then pretended to confide in him that there was one thing that might ruin her plans. It was the fear of making a terrible mistake by giving some customer the wrong medicine.

"For example," she said, "those ones that some kids take for—what's it called when there's a problem with one of the glands?"

"Which gland?" he asked.

"Oh, I don't know." She shrugged.

"Thyroid?"

"All right, that one. What color are the pills for it, white?"

"Pink," he corrected her.

"So let's say pink then." She gave him a worried look. "Now aren't there some other pink ones for some other condition? If the person with that gland problem took *them*, could they make him have a heart attack or something?"

"It could happen, I suppose," the druggist said thoughtfully. "But not if you just check the prescriptions against the labels on the containers we keep them in."

"Oh, come on," Alicia murmured, stepping up to the high counter he was standing behind and just happening to let her fingers come down on the back of his hand. "I mean, imagine that this was a murder movie and you had to find some poison. Don't tell me you couldn't come up with a really good one?"

It must have been her leaning in closer that started him stuttering. "Oh, w-w-well, for a movie, maybe there might be s-something up there on that shelf," he said.

"Which ones?" she asked, coming behind the counter with her eyes wide as saucers.

"Any of them, actually," he said, backing away. "Look, your father wouldn't like this. Anyway, I've got a girlfriend, and you're way too young for me, okay?"

"Don't worry," she purred. "I won't tell anybody if you give me a little kiss."

"Well, you know, Alice—"

"Alicia."

"Yeah. Alicia. That's not the way I do things. No offense, okay?"

"Hey, no problem. I just like to be playful, that's all. Do you mind if I make a phone call before I take off?"

"Sure," he said with relief. "Go ahead."

Alicia went toward the phone on the wall over the counter. As she picked up the receiver, she said, "This is sort of private, okay?"

"That's fine," he said. Lifting a case of shaving cream cans from the floor, he went up front to arrange a display.

The moment he was out of sight, Alicia darted to the shelf where the dangerous pills were kept, opened a big stoppered bottle, grabbed a handful, stuffed them in her pocket, and ran back to the phone. By the time he returned, she was hanging up.

"You know, I'm feeling kind of embarrassed about this, what with you thinking I was flirting and all," Alicia said.

"Don't worry about it," he said.

"Well, that's awfully hard, because you might say something to my dad."

"Not a chance."

"Couldn't you just forget I even came in here?"

"Absolutely," he said. "And good luck on that Homecoming thing."

"Oh, I think people make their own luck," Alicia declared. With a confident smile, she headed for the door.

Once she left the store, I couldn't see her until she

turned the tiny mirror jutting off the left handlebar of my bike away from the traffic coming up behind her. She actually wanted to ask *me* where Wendy's house was so she could go there with the poison.

"Do you really think I'd tell you?"

"Don't mess with me," she warned fiercely.

"Why? What else can you do to me after you kill my best friend?"

Alicia's expression grew hard as stone. "I could kill your parents."

That shook me up totally at first. But while we were bouncing along on the road, I was able to say, "Maybe you could, but you won't. You need them too much to love you."

I could see that I'd gotten her thinking, and it gave me a moment's hope that I could reach her. "Alicia," I said with more kindness toward her than I knew was in me, "in some ways you're still just a child. You don't know what death really is."

"I know what it is," she said harshly.

"No, you don't," I insisted. "You haven't been in real life long enough. Learning about life comes gradually, in bits and pieces, to someone who has existed only in mirrors. I can imagine what it must have been like for you to finally enter a world where a person can actually *do* things, make things happen, have some control and *power!*"

Was I catching a thoughtful look in Alicia's eye?

In the glare of streetlights it was hard to tell, but I continued trying to reason with her. "So naturally I understand how resentful you might be when Wendy or anyone else seems to be trying to stop you from getting your way."

"She *is* trying to get in my way," Alicia hissed.

"You don't know that for sure. You make a lot of your own troubles."

"Yes? Well, I can *un*make them, too, and I will! I've had enough of this preaching. If you're not going to show me where she lives, I'll find it out for myself. Over and out!"

She shoved the mirror away.

I still don't know what trick of my mind helped me follow her—maybe I was only filling the black emptiness with my imagination. Yet I seemed to see Alicia pedaling the bike under streetlamps and peering closely at the names on mailboxes. I seemed to see her stop near the driveway of Wendy's house, park the bike out of sight behind a tree, and sneak through the shrubs that surrounded the property.

While it couldn't have been much later than seven-thirty or so, the house was dark and she probably hadn't seen any cars. If the family was out to dinner, then here was her chance to slip inside and replace Wendy's medicine with the poison!

All of a sudden I was reflecting her! Behind me, a light had blazed on, and the lower part of the window

I was now on went shooting upward. "Who's there!" boomed a voice that made Alicia jump back, gasping. The gigantic shoulders and balding head of Wendy's father pushed out over the sill below me.

"It's some kid," he said, starting to make her out. "Is that you, Alice?"

"Mr. Bauer, you frightened me," she said meekly, still catching her breath.

"What are you doing back there?"

"I wanted to talk to Wendy. But then at the door I got afraid because I was told not to come here. So I thought maybe if I could knock on her window . . ."

"Just a minute," he told her, and ducked back inside. Then Mrs. Bauer came to the window.

"We're not ogres," she called out. "There's no need to be afraid of us, Alice. But Wendy went to bed early and—"

"I was only reading, Mom!" Wendy interrupted from inside the house. "Besides, how could I sleep after *this*? Please let her come in!"

Then I was off to nowhere again. By the time I came back, on the living-room mirror, it was just as I expected. Wendy was in tears, and she and Alicia were embracing. Alicia was apologizing a mile a minute for being such a fool and a bad friend. She said over and over again how ashamed she was of all the selfish, mean, cruel, and spiteful things she had said and done!

It was a ridiculous performance, and nothing could have been more phony than Alicia's attempts at matching Wendy sob for sob. But I already knew how heartless she really was. As far as I was concerned, there was no more excusing that Unformed *thing* that had now become a *monster!* There was now real danger to Wendy. Even more desperately than I had at the movies, I tried to signal Wendy. But nothing, absolutely nothing, changed. I was still trying when they blanked me out to go upstairs to talk in Wendy's room.

Suddenly I was back. And this time—oh, no!— Alicia and I were in Wendy's bathroom. She was going through the cabinet looking for the right medicine bottle.

And she found it!

I don't recall now what I sputtered, what kind of begging and pleading I did as she quickly dumped out pills and put in others. But she cut me off with a rattlesnake hiss.

"Shut up and don't bug me, Alice. That attack on you in the darkness was only a little punishment for getting out of line. If I had wanted the Unformed to destroy you, they would have."

"It's my friend's life that counts now," I told her. "And I'm going to stop you."

She smirked as she put the cap back on the bottle and said simply, "Not tonight you won't."

I'm sorry to say, Alicia was right. There wasn't a thing I could do. After Alicia went back to my house, she called Wendy's mother to thank everyone again and to say good night to Wendy.

She listened anxiously to Mrs. Bauer's reply and then relaxed, saying, "Oh, Wendy's asleep already? That's okay. I'll see her tomorrow in school."

But as she put down the receiver, Alicia added to herself, "If she ever gets there, that is."

My ride to school the next day was filled with dread. I could see Alicia was nervous, too. She sat down with David, but they had nothing to say to each other. By the time she got off the bus, her face was hard as stone.

Meanwhile, something about me was definitely changing. I could feel it. Looking back now at this turning point, I realize that I had stopped wasting my precious energy on feeling sorry for myself. All my thoughts were focused on one thing only: finding some way to save Wendy!

To Alicia's shock and disappointment, Wendy was still alive and standing, although she was so woozy that she had to lean against her locker to keep from falling. Right away, Alicia made a big show of concern and wanted to know what was the matter.

"I don't know," Wendy answered slowly. "I was feeling a little dizzy before I left the house. Mom said maybe I shouldn't go to school, but I've got tests and I thought I'd be okay. Now my head's whirling like a top, and I feel so strange."

"Uh-oh. Must be one of those twenty-four-hour viruses that are going around," Alicia told her, while some other girls who were hanging around agreed.

"I . . . I don't think so," Wendy said. She seemed to be having trouble breathing. "This . . . this is different. It's kind of scary, Alice. I mean, Alicia."

"Oh, I don't care what you call me! I just care what's happening to you. Look, maybe you ought to go home now. I'll go with you to the nurse, okay?"

"I don't know," said Wendy uncertainly. "I don't want them calling my mother and getting her worried. Maybe I can just take it easy through first period. It's only Study Hall anyway."

Alicia seemed terribly frustrated. For a moment I wondered why. Then suddenly I knew! If Wendy was going to be taken to the hospital, Alicia wanted it to be from the house rather than from school. If it was from the house—and if Alicia was to go home with her first—then she'd have no problem slipping back into Wendy's bathroom, dumping what was left of the bad pills down the toilet, and replacing them with the good ones she had taken out.

But it didn't work out that way. We wouldn't see Wendy again until Signing. All through Social Studies, I watched Alicia gritting her teeth anxiously.

Meanwhile, I passed my time by experimenting with what, if anything, I could control by using the force of my mind. Could I, for example, move anything on somebody's desk? A loose sheet of paper? A pen?

I'll tell you what I did manage to do. The windows were closed, there was no fan going, and yet that expensive silk scarf around Alicia's neck—one of the many things she'd gotten David to buy her—was starting to flutter.

But was this going to make any difference in Signing class? I couldn't see how. First, being able to perform this particular trick didn't mean I'd be able to move my arms in front of Wendy. Second, even if I could, nothing in the classroom remotely resembled a mirror. Wendy certainly wasn't likely to look at some stupid clock's face up on the wall!

But Alicia herself gave me my chance. Less than ten minutes after Signing started, Alicia got up from her seat and announced that her friend looked much too sick to go on with class and that she personally was going to take her to the nurse.

Nobody objected. Wendy looked bad enough, with her face as gray as a sunless day and her eyes practically swimming in her head.

So Alicia helped her walk to the nurse's office, and there I was as large as life on a shiny mirror that reflected them both. Praying that I could actually do this and motivated by the need to save Wendy's life, I began to move my own arms differently from Alicia. First I made the sign for "I love you." Then I signaled Wendy with finger-spelling and repeated three times that her medicine had been changed by Alicia and she was being poisoned!

"I think she's going straight to the hospital," said the nurse. She picked up the intercom to notify the office.

Wendy was staring at me, but in such a strange, bleary-eyed way that I couldn't tell whether she'd actually seen anything. Even if she had, she might think that her eyes were playing tricks on her. As it was, they rolled backward and went totally white. Then a thin whitish foam, like bubbling dishwasher detergent, spewed from her mouth. Her body stiffened like a board, and she fell to the floor.

Chapter 13

An ambulance rushed Wendy to the hospital, and Alicia was sent back to her classes. I expected her to make sure that everyone saw a terribly concerned expression on her face. But that's not what happened. Her face simply went blank. She didn't answer anybody's questions about Wendy, and she was so absentminded that I realized she couldn't stop thinking about those unused pills in the Bauer house.

At home that night, while my mom was on the phone learning that Wendy was in a coma, Alicia listened carefully to everything that was said. The doctors were still waiting for the test results, but they were pretty sure Wendy's condition was caused by something she had ingested.

The next morning, Wendy was still holding on. So that's exactly what I did when Alicia went to school, dragging me along on mirrors like Mary's little lamb.

But now a real change in Alicia's behavior was developing. It started slowly and grew all day, then continued in the days that followed. She seemed lightheaded and giddy. Sometimes she even giggled. I mean, she was really off the wall. Teachers and kids stared at her, and some of them must have been wondering if she was taking drugs.

The most confusing thing was the way she started acting toward me. I was still being ignored, of course. There was never a single word to me or even a direct look, and yet Alicia kept sneaking quick and nervous glances my way. I couldn't figure it out until it reminded me of a little child who knows she's been very naughty. Then it came to me with a jolt—Alicia might be showing the beginnings of a conscience. Even if it was a guilty one.

A guilty conscience could also explain why she had resisted my mother's offers to take her to the hospital to see Wendy. When at last my mother confronted her about this after dinner one night, saying she couldn't understand all these excuses, there was an explosion.

"I don't see what's so strange about it! I just don't like to look at *sick* people!" Alicia cried.

"But this is *Wendy!*"

"So? She's unconscious! She won't even know I was there."

"But *you'd* know it, Alice."

"I've told you and I've told you, my name is Alicia!"

"Frankly," declared my father, "we're not so sure we prefer the daughter who calls herself Alicia to the one we had before."

That brought Alicia to her feet. "What do you mean?" she demanded in a tight and breathless voice.

"I mean," said my father, "you were less concerned with yourself than you are now."

Alicia had feared the worst, so now she breathed easier. But the insult was still out there. "Oh, I see. You like the Alice who spent all her time counting new pimples in mirrors and hating herself for how she looked!"

"We're not saying that," my mom said reassuringly. "But what would you do, Alicia, if something happened to one of us? A major illness, or a terrible accident? Wouldn't you go to the hospital to see me or your father?"

"Don't talk like that! Nothing's going to happen to either of you," Alicia protested.

"In life, you can never be sure of these things," said my father. "I guess about the only thing you *can* be sure of is love."

"Love! Love! Love!" stormed Alicia, rushing toward the stairs. "Everybody's always talking about it, but is there anyone who loves *me*?"

I couldn't see my parents just then, but I could feel how stunned they were. "Stop right there!" my mother shouted. "What has gotten into you lately?"

Midway up the steps, Alicia grabbed the banister and pulled herself together. When she swung around again, she was all sweetness and sorrow.

"I'm sorry. I really am," she murmured. Her lower lip trembled so hard that she had to bite down on it before she could go on again. "I guess I've been acting without feeling lately. But please try to see how much I'm going through because of what's happened to Wendy. I just know that when I look at her in that hospital bed, I'll feel so helpless and . . ."

"Oh, my poor baby," exclaimed my mother before violins could start playing in the background for this Academy Award performance.

"My fault for misjudging you," said my father. "Come on down here for hugs all around."

Of course Alicia was downstairs in a flash. Then the phone rang. I had the strangest feeling about that call, and it bothered me that so many rings were left unanswered. At last my mother pulled away from Alicia's embrace to pick up the phone.

Soon she was listening intently. "Yes, yes," she sang out. "Really? Oh, that's such good news! Sitting up and what? And eating too! Why, that's wonderful! What's that? She does? Oh, certainly. Yes, of course!"

"Is this about Wendy?" my father asked, though that was certainly clear to Alicia, who had frozen into a breathless statue.

"Yes. Alicia, Wendy's mother says Wendy can't wait to see you. She wants you to come right over."

"Now? But I—no, I couldn't possibly. I have to do my home . . ."

My father glared at her, and she withered. "All right." Alicia darted a few anxious looks at the shinier surfaces in the room, trying to locate me. But I gave her back only blank looks. I wanted to make her feel how completely on her own she really was, regardless of the fact that both my parents were going to the hospital with her.

In the car, I caught glimpses of Alicia from the rearview mirror. At first she seemed very worried. As time went on, however, and she noticed me studying her, that cool and confident little smile returned. She'd plastered it there to show me how completely in control of herself she was. I think she was starting to feel that she had nothing to worry about. Although Wendy was still alive, Alicia had gotten her out of the way long enough so that she couldn't spoil the vote for Homecoming Queen. All she needed to do now was to pretend to be happy about Wendy's recovery.

Alicia's confidence didn't surprise me. What really got my attention was that my father was muttering to himself—mumbling something in the preoccupied way that always sent my mother up the wall.

"You're swallowing your words again," she complained. "What about Wendy's medication?"

"Nothing," said my dad. "But Brian told me something disturbing last week, and I put it out of my mind because . . . well, I didn't want to think about it."

"What was it?"

"Well, just that somebody had come into the pharmacy and asked him about the drug Wendy takes. It seems this person wanted to know what could be substituted for it that would have the effect of a poison."

"Oh, my God! Who was he?"

"Not a he."

"You honestly think that—"

"No, no," my father said hastily. "Just a disturbing thought, that's all."

"You didn't tell me who it was," she persisted.

"It was me, Mom!" confessed Alicia.

"You?" My mother spun around in her seat. "But *why*?"

"I just went in to tease Brian, that's all. He's always so serious." Alicia forced herself to giggle. "He thought I liked him. And I do, in a friendly way."

"I swear, Alicia. Sometimes I think you're out of control," my mother was almost screaming.

Alicia grew solemn. "I think it's called being an adolescent, Mom. But I'll try to behave better from now on." Alicia paused. My father had been shaking his head during all this. "What is it, Dad? Do you think I'm a would-be murderer?"

"Of course not! Don't be silly."

"What then?"

"I could lose my license to dispense medicine if

there's even the slightest hint that my pharmacy might have given out a drug illegally. But it's over, I suppose. Let's just drop it."

The car was turning into the hospital parking lot. Alicia had forgotten that the compact was on her lap. It slipped to the floor, still open, when she got up to go inside.

There weren't many shiny places from which I could keep an eye on her while they were walking through the corridors. But then all at once I was on the window of Wendy's room, reflecting Alicia coming in with my folks. A cop in uniform was there, too. And *that,* I could see, gave Alicia one heck of a jolt.

My parents immediately recognized him as Wendy's brother, and Alicia relaxed a bit when he got up to shake hands with my dad and offer my mom his chair. The hello he gave Alicia, though, had something in it that sounded more like a policeman than an older brother.

The tone of his voice shook Alicia up again. But then she stepped past him, went to the head of the bed, and started making nice to Wendy.

Most of the "how are you feeling" questions, though, were handled by my mother. I'm sure that Alicia was relieved to have as little to say as possible. As for Wendy, even though she was cheerful and very glad to be getting well, she was paler than I'd ever seen her, and her voice was still weak.

After a while, she smiled and said, "I'd like to be alone with my friend."

The way she came down on the word *friend* reminded me of the hello her brother had given Alicia. He waited until my parents went out. Then, at a gesture from Wendy, he went to a drawer by her bedside and took out a hand mirror. She pointed to where she wanted it, and he rolled a medicine stand to the spot and set the mirror on top. "Like that, Sis?"

"Perfect," Wendy answered.

Her brother nodded solemnly and quickly left the room, closing the door behind him.

And it was perfect, because at the very instant he put the mirror in place, I leaped onto its surface, where both Wendy and Alicia could see me. By then—oh joy!—I was absolutely certain that Wendy *had* seen me signal to her in the school nurse's office. Even with her growing dizziness she had understood.

When Wendy made the "I love you" sign directly to me and I signed back, Alicia went crazy. She rushed to the mirror and knocked me down.

Then came the final attack of the Unformed! They swarmed on top of me from everywhere: clawing, biting, ripping. Yet I was stronger than they were.

"Take off!" I commanded. "There's no way you can pull me apart, no matter what you do. Because you guys aren't real—but I *am!*"

Suddenly the Unformed were gone, and I found

myself back in the hospital room. While I'd been gone, I learned later on, Wendy had told Alicia, "My brother's just outside the door, and there's another policeman downstairs. Don't make me angrier than I already am. Pick that mirror up. I want Alice to hear every word of this."

So I was put back into place, and Wendy began again. "This is going to be short, Alicia, because I don't need any lies from you. The last thing I want is a bunch of simpering apologies. I know what you did. My brother took the rest of the pills to a lab to have them analyzed. And I've got to say, for a cool operator who was smart enough to trick a human being out of her own place in life, you were pretty stupid to pull a stunt like that."

Wendy grinned and went on. "Now, if this sounds like I've rehearsed all my words, well, I have. It's given me so much pleasure going over and over them that I've grown healthier and healthier doing it. Here's how everything stands. You are going to change places with Alice right away. Either that or you're going to be arrested and put in jail. In this state, even a fifteen-year-old can be tried as an adult for a serious crime. This was attempted murder, Alicia, and your nonsense ends right now."

"I can't let it end now," Alicia howled. "I have to be Homecoming Queen!"

"Too bad! I said *now*," Wendy insisted.

Alicia folded her arms, sneering. "If you have me arrested, it'll come out where I got the pills. Alice's father will lose his license!"

Wendy looked at me, and I nodded.

"The voting will be tomorrow," Alicia went on, "and the crowning is the Saturday after this, just before the football game. Let me win the crown and wear it during the game. After that, I'll do whatever you want."

Once again, Wendy looked at me, and again I nodded. "You'd better," she warned Alicia. "Because after that, absolutely nothing will stop my real friend from having her own life back. Now get out of here!"

As we drove home, my father mentioned how surprised he was that Wendy didn't seem very friendly to Alicia.

"Well, they still have some unsettled issues," declared my mother. "But I'm sure it'll work out, right, darling?"

"Oh, sure," grunted Alicia.

"So you're not all that down in the dumps, are you?"

"Well, I am, but I won't be for long," Alicia said. Her voice hardened. "I can promise you that."

"Good," sighed my father. But I had exactly the opposite reaction.

That night, I made the bathroom mirror crack

open, but I couldn't actually see anything. I must have been reflecting only the lump Alicia made under the bedcovers. She was using my old trick of pulling the phone underneath the covers with her. By straining hard to hear, I realized she was talking to the man who used to manage David's band. I think she was asking him about his lawyer. Right away, I could tell what was on her mind. As a matter of fact, things grew so clear to me, I almost suspected I had jumped straight into her thoughts!

Alicia was trying to find out if somebody as young as she was would have to go to jail if she was convicted. Since this would be the first time she had ever gotten into trouble, couldn't she just get probation or something?

Apparently the man said that there was no way to be completely sure. Then she asked how long the jail time would have to be.

Alicia listened and thanked him a lot before hanging up. It was obvious to me that Alicia had made up her mind to risk going to jail rather than give me back my life.

From her point of view, it really did make sense to tough it out. After all, no prison in the world could be worse than spending the rest of her existence on mirrors.

Chapter 14

The days went by. Naturally I didn't get to see Wendy. Alicia was not about to pay any more visits to the hospital or turn up at the Bauers' house after my friend was allowed to go home.

Meanwhile, the Homecoming Queen votes were counted, and though it was a squeaker all the way, Alicia won. Now that no one could stop her from putting on the crown just before the last game, Alicia let her real personality show.

She began lording it over the people who looked up to her, made cruel fun of the Student Body, and even told David DeWitt off in front of his whole team. He might be a hero on the football field, she said, but he was just a boring little boy. She had decided that she was going to become a famous fashion model.

I remained quiet in the nothingness, not bothered by any of the Unformed, and concentrated entirely on getting mentally ready for that one moment when I might yet have my chance to foil Alicia's plans. It came just before she left for the football stadium to be crowned queen. She was walking into the bathroom for a look at the outfit my parents had practically mortgaged the house to buy for her. At that moment I ended my long, self-imposed silence.

"Alicia, I just want to say that I may hate you, but I can't help admiring your guts."

Her eyebrows lifted. "Really?"

"Yes. I'm so glad I'm not changing places with you until *after* the crowning. I could never go up there considering . . ."

"Considering what? What are you talking about?"

"Oh, that's right. You can't look into mirrors to see your own face. You only see me."

"So? What about it?"

"Alicia, don't you know? You're all broken out."

"Oh, sure." She gave a little laugh of disbelief.

"Have it your own way," I told her. "Why should I care?"

She was worried now, and frowning. "You're crazy!"

"Okay, I'm crazy," I said with a shrug.

"Hold on! Are you trying to tell me that all of a sudden—"

"Well, yes and no, Alicia. I had the feeling this was going to happen when you started sweating in the hospital while Wendy was talking. You really were anxious then, and all your cool was gone. I thought it might happen then, only you got through it all right. So I didn't pay any attention until—"

Alicia cut me off. She had no patience for this at all. "What are you *claiming* that you see now?"

"Hey, I don't *claim* anything," I said very offhandedly. "But for your information, your face is as bad as it ever was with me."

"You're not trying to tell me that I've got a few *pimples?*"

"A *few?* They're all over your face. Whiteheads. Blackheads. Look, I'm sorry. I thought you knew. Otherwise I wouldn't have—"

"Shut up! Shut up!" Closing in on the mirror, Alicia's widening eyes seemed to be counting my eruptions. "No, it's not possible that I could look like you! There is no way I could ever be this hideous!"

Since I'd been ordered not to speak, I simply raised my eyebrows and forced myself to grin. I think it was that angelic-looking smile that got her. When she gave me a look of stark terror, I knew that this split second—before her darting hands could examine the clear and perfect skin she still had—was the time for me to spring on top of her from the glass. Yet somehow I couldn't act fast enough. My fears had taken some of my strength and slowed me down. I did not leap on her as she had twice leaped on me. Helplessly, I watched her touch her face. What had ever made me think I could do this? It was hopeless— and so was my chance to live again.

But then the miracle happened—pimples sprouted! There weren't many. Maybe there weren't even any. I personally didn't see a single one. But from the growing horror in Alicia's eyes, I knew that she felt them!

"No, this can't be!" she yowled. "This cannot happen to *me!* Not when thousands of people are going to see me put on the crown. Not when I'll be on TV and my picture will be in the newspapers! Not when my whole future—"

"I have to tell you, Alicia, that you don't have any," I said. And tensing for the fight that would save my life, I sailed out of the mirror like a diver from a springboard. She fell back as I somehow invaded her physical reality.

Choking, she cried out, "What are you doing?"

"Taking over!" I sang inside our head.

"Get out of me!" she screamed, flailing the empty air outside our body with her arms, as if that would do any good.

I was fighting for control of each muscle and every cell in our brain. The whole of my physical self was a battlefield—and I would simply not let myself lose.

"It's over for you," I bellowed over the beating of my heart. At first the words were only a thought. But when I regained control of my lungs, the words went flying from my mouth. "Over, Alicia! Over! *Leave my body!*"

"Alice," she croaked as if she was strangling. "Please listen to me! We'll share it. I know you were ready to do that before."

"Too late," I answered, knowing that I had just won the most important battle of my life.

"But I've helped you!"

"You trapped me and you hurt my friend."

"Forgive me. I can learn. I can—"

"Good-bye, Alicia!"

I heard a wrenching sob and a moan. Then a wild shriek that faded farther and farther away before trailing off somewhere beyond the realm of mirrors.

She was gone now. I found myself—totally Alice again!—standing in that silly outfit my poor parents had spent a fortune to buy. I walked down the stairs telling myself that I was home, home, *home!*

On our way to the stadium, I asked that we stop first at Wendy's house.

"Are you sure?" said my mother, who still hadn't completely gotten over her funny feelings about Mrs. Bauer.

"Very!"

Mom and Dad stayed in the car while I started up the walk. Wendy must have seen me coming from the living-room window, because she opened the door before I could ring the bell. I didn't have to tell her that I was back in my own body. She knew the real me as only best friends can know each other.

•I made the "I Love You" sign. She made it back, and we both began laughing and crying at the same time.

Read these other great thrillers

by

Larry Weinberg

Ghost Hotel

ISBN 0-8167-3420-8

Return to Ghost Hotel

ISBN 0-8167-4016-X

Escape from Ghost Hotel

ISBN 0-8167-4508-0

Available wherever you buy books.